The Skeeter Daddle Diaries

Reflections of a South End Nettle Farmer

By Jack Archibald

ACKNOWLEDGEMENTS

I would like to express my thanks to Joyce Lukaczer for her encouragement, design, layout and editing of this book. I want to offer a heartfelt thank you to the South End String Band who for years have endured and indulged these commentaries at our concerts full knowing they could be playing another song instead. I also want to thank the folks here on the South End, good neighbors pretty much and, if not, interesting characters. And mostly I want to give profound thanks to Karen Prasse, the 'mizzus' and my best friend, the woman who gave Skeeter all the latitude in the world to live his life the only way he probably could and who meant what she said the day we got married, "for rich or for poor," not knowing they would be the same thing.

ON THE WEB

www.southendweb.net
www.southendstringband.com
www.revisionaryglassworks.com

I would like to dedicate this book to my old friend Joe McCrea, one of the original Piranha Brothers who, for a few years, lived with Ruby and me on the wild South End when money was scarce and jobs were scarcer. Back in the early days, he showed me by example that art and music and life are really one and the same. And more importantly, that they can be learned. There's an old Van Morrison song that says, *"There are guides and spirits all along the way who will befriend us…"* Joe was one of those.

The Diaries

Camano or Bust: Homesteading the Backwash

Gators in the Kiddie Pool

Free Range Clams: Political Correctness Unleashed

Suburbanites at the Gate: Backhoe Archeology

Apocalypse Then: After the Rapture

The Visuals

Section One

Section Two

Section Three

Section Four

Camano or Bust: Homesteading the Backwash

We are stardust, we are golden,
And we got to get ourselves back to the Garden.

Joni Mitchell

*"The South End was a poor man's paradise back then. You'd
have to be a rich man now to live here."*

Ted Snowden, builder of Tyee Grocery and the 5 acre wrecking yard behind it.
He and his wife Ellen ran the tow trucks, a gyppo well drilling outfit and were
basically the entirety of legal capitalism in these backwashes for 20 years.

Backwash Beginnings

When I first came to the South End, folks I knew in the Big City—no, not Stanwoodopolis—Seattle and Gomorrah—they said don't move there. It's the end of the earth. There's no services, no shopping, no nothing. One friend told me she'd broke down down there and thought she'd never get off that damned island. She figured only a fool or a hermit would move to a place so desolate. She was right.

I was a fresh-faced, wide-eyed, shallow-pockets homesteader. The mizzus took one look at our leaky, plastic-instead-of-windows shack and sat down and cried herself a river. Before she left me. She could recognize a sinking ship when she saw one and she wasn't one for waiting for the storms.

I didn't have a job at the time. Didn't have many skills either. Couldn't frame a house or fix a machine or operate equipment. I figured that's what I was here to learn. I figured right. For once.

The South End, for those who ask where exactly *is* it, the South End is a metaphor. That, chillun, is what happens when an unemployed English teacher heads to the hills and finds himself in the nettle ravines of backwash America. The South End, to this sad sodbuster, wasn't a place so much as an opportunity for redemption, a clean start, a frontier at the edge of a continent at the fringes of a frayed psyche. Nettle farming looked pretty good.

The South End still exists. It's a tad more crowded and it's gone slightly upscale compared to my shack days. But the truth is, The South End may look like the end of the line to some, but it's still mostly a journey in search of a place that looks like Home. A place where we built our cabins, grew our gardens, fertilized our fables, learned our trades, played our music and fashioned our lives. It's a journey worth taking, I've come to believe, looking back through the years. We all got a South End, you stop and think about it. So take your shoes off, wiggle your toes and walk a spell with us down a familiar path. I think you'll recognize it pretty quick…

Island Fever

A lot of folks ask if we get Island Fever down at the South End all cooped up on that butt-end of a skinny little island at the far side of the American continent isolated from the rest of the modern world. TV reception's bad and cable doesn't reach us and the nearest cell phone tower is over on the mainland.

People figure, I guess, we moved this far away from shopping malls and suburbs and fast food joints by Accident. We must've thought Camano City was sort of Eldorado with streets of gold and free gas. Or that we drove through Stanwoodopolis on a dark and stormy night when we got lost and ended up out of fuel on the South End and decided it would be easier to homestead than find a phone booth and call the nearest tow truck.

The South End does sit right smack flat at the end of America. Or the beginning as we like to think. Some of the old pioneer spirit still remains down here. You never know, we just might need it again. We chop our heat, we crab and clam and fish and grow some of our dinners, we make our boats, we build our cabins, we repair our cars, our trucks, our well pumps, our tractors, ourselves, we make our own shine, our own wine, our own music and our own entertainment.

We *all* used to do this. It wasn't something special. Now most folks can't imagine it. They can't imagine much of anything... TV took care of that.

They say the world's shrunk down a little in these fast paced times. About 21 inches diagonal, I'd say. Internet, satellites, global travel, the whole she-bang bringing us all closer together, one big happy-deal grinning family at the golden arches of the world. I admit I came here to the end of this island to get away. A lot of us did. A lot of us still do. The South End's not real big, about the size of our imagination. But some of the back porches down here go on nearly forever.

Archipelago Apartheid

There are islands and then there are islands. Manhattan's an island, but the real estate agents bulldozed down its palm trees long ago. A lot of islands are isolated, a bump in the sea. Some islands hang out together. Geologists call them an archipelago. The islands by us didn't get invited into the San Juan Archipelago Club. I think they knew we'd put bridges up and drive right on like we weren't proud to *be* an island. Naw, we wanted an umbilical to the mainland.

A Real Island sneers at the idea of the Mainland. A real islander doesn't commute to a job back on the Mainland. A real archipelagist doesn't shop at the Safeway on the Mainland. An honest-to-God rock hugging, brine snorting, bent back barnacle covered island hermit doesn't jump on a ferry every chance he gets so he can stand on Terra Firma in the Wal Mart parking lot.

A Real Islander is hoping deep down in his seaweed filled boots that the Tectonic Plates are moving him *out* past the Straits, out past Dungeness Spit, out past Neah Bay, out past the 3-mile territorial limits. A Real Islander came, not so much to Come to an Island, as to *leave* the Mainland, physically, spiritually and meta-damn-phorically. They're Escapists. They're refugees from

Real Life. Or what Mainlanders call Whack Jobs. Take your preference.

Our island hedges its bets. Way up at the cold north end, folks hardly know they're *on* an island. They can drive in to work at Boeing, shop at Costco, grab a Big Mac and be home in time for Baywatch re-runs on cable any day of the month. Down in the equatorial jungles of the South End, we're unemployed, the drive just to the bridge is too horrible to contemplate, the only fast food we got is growing in our gardens and TV reception's so poor we only got first run junk.

When the earthquake knocks down our puny little bridge, we'll have some folks real surprised to learn they're finally gonna have to make a choice. Course, when they build the South End Bridge to Everett, we will too.

Mail Order Bride

Now the mizzus was a sort of mail order bride. I came out to the rainforests here in the 70's, bought my 7 acres and my mule just before the interest rates went wild and discovered how few single ladies there were in the woods of the South End.

So I resorted to what our pioneer ancestors turned to... no, not *that*... I wrote back to the Midwest for a wife. I had a lady friend in Minnysota who was just fixing to graduate with her masters degree in librarying. Librarying, I thought to myself, is even better'n school ma'arm. She could teach some of the artists on the South End here how to read and write and then we could sit around the porch and discuss Nietzsche and Tolstoy, and the events of the day.

Late spring of 1981 I commenced to writing heart wrenching, bodice ripping, pulse pounding love letters. I told my darling all about our little island, how it was a tropical paradise where our beautiful cottage nestled in the arms of million year old cedar trees and coconut palms and you could see the Olympic Mountains every night at sunset glowing like a fireplace and that old sun had nothing on the lovelight in my heart for her...

Course she didn't have a chance... Who could resist my literary charms? And I'm sure she carried a picture of my irresistible self in a locket in her bosom, pining—*pining*, ladies and gentlemen—for that day a letter would arrive from her Prince Charming, old lumber Jack himself, king of Camano, practically Paul Bunyan with a book of poems under his ax-wielding arm.

Well, I was surprised *too* that she didn't rush out to my waiting muscle bound arms. So I wrote some more. I wrote a dictionary worth. Then I wrote an Encyclopedia Britannica. Spring turned to summer, summer turned to fall, fall became winter, my dreams turned to mush. I run outa words, *me!* With nothing left to say. I was about to give up and become a Zen hermit priest.

But one day I got a letter saying she was coming out… For a day or two, then going to Alaska to see her cousin. Alaska? Why on god's green earth would she go to a godforsaken hellhole like that when she could have the whole South End paradise?

Course she was gonna see the cottage wasn't a cottage—it was a shack. Leaky roof, crooked floors, a ladder to the upstairs. Alaska was gonna look *real* good. And Prince Charming? I was in serious trouble now.

But luck was on my side. The day she flew in a storm took out a dozen trees to the South End and power was out when we pulled in the drive. So I lit up the oil lamps and popped the champagne and boiled the crabs on the woodstove and I won't tell you the details but let your romantic imagination run wild and you might have some small notion of why the mizzus is still the mizzus and why we both still celebrate the day she came out here and not our wedding anniversary and why the South End will always be a tropical paradise to at least a couple of us old lovebirds.

Hard Times

When I first got off the boat at the South End, I was what you called Dirt Poor. The homestead was played out, logged off, washed up and fallen down… Which is why it was so cheap. But even so, I gave everything I had to buy it. Everything.

Most of us back then on the remote shores of the South End were poor. No shame in that. We lived in shacks and trailers, we worked odd jobs when they were available, we learned to make do, get by, scratch it out. We bartered and traded, grew gardens, raised chickens and goats, planted orchards, fished, crabbed, clammed. Everybody did.

I met people who dropped an engine like they did it every day. Rebuild it, put it back in. People who built their own house, stud by stud, nail by nail. People who sewed their own clothes. People who made their jams and preserves. Their wines and beer. People who made their own music. Their own instruments. Those folks convinced me—a boy who didn't know a socket wrench from a framing square—I might be able to do the same thing.

That was the culture down here. Folks ask if life was hard. I never thought it was. Hard is doing what you don't love. Hard is boredom. Hard is an emptiness that won't fill. Hard is too much time on your hands.

Down at the South End life wasn't hard. It was full up. In the end all those poor neighbors of mine showed me how to make most everything and how to make the most of everything. Mostly, though, they showed me how to make my life mine. And cornball as it sounds, that's why us dirt poor pioneers of the South End never thought of ourselves as anything but rich…

Chicken Channel

Now the South End's got its own economics. Being how there's no work, no industry, no banks and no investment firms, we've had to resort to alternative fiduciary strategies. Course I'm talking about bartering. You know, good old fashioned horse trading. Bartering's an age-old tradition on the South End. It's a cousin of stealing and an uncle of lying. When it's working right, both ends of the trade feel like they cheated the other guy blind.

I got my first banjo in a swap for a .22 Remington rifle I didn't want any more. Most of my illegal building structures are erected from bartered lumber, doors, windows and the like. I've traded boats and cars and pickups. Hell, I'd probably swap the muzzus if I weren't so fretful she'd get the short end of the stick...

Course on the South End you'll run into fellas who know the horse-trading game a whole lot better'n you. And I don't mean just the artists. I was trading an old boy for some chickens when I first arrived and I was putting together my barnyard petting zoo. Chickens and a rear end for my Chevy half ton. He lived up some holler in a one room tarpaper house and lived completely off what he gleaned from the old dump. He had a TV showroom set up out in the drive: black and whites, color, consoles, cabinets with or without hi-fi, whole entertainment centers. The chickens were there too, watching sixteen of their fav-o-rite programs. I said I'd take a dozen if they were good layers. He said, hoo boy, get ready for an omelet and we commenced to chasing chickens from CBS to the outhouse, from NBC to the barn. Stuffed em cackling and flapping into a burlap sack.

We counted em out at the end and this old boy says *lookee* here and damned if he doesn't pull two eggs out. Them's real layers, he says with half his teeth missing. Course I was real pleased with this trade right from the get-go. Oldest trick in the book. Guess I never read the book. You all know, I suspect, I never got another egg and those old banty hens, being one hundred years old, was way too tough to eat. After awhile I just settled down n' let em watch TV.

Career Choices

The South End isn't what most folks would call High Falutin. Money's usually been scarce as dentists are for chickens. We're about the last place in Puget Sound without an Expresso Stand two blocks away. No, we live on modest incomes you might say. When times get real tough we hunker down and claim to be artists and boatbuilders and musicians and the like. You can always tell a fella's down on his luck when he starts calling his shack a studio. That boy's gonna be trouble...

There aren't many jobs on the South End. The factories have all closed down and moved to where the labor's cheap; you know, places like Concrete and Bow-Edison. The businesses are boarded up, the fishing's ruined, the trees are all cut down. Truth is, there never was any work down here and some folks find that odd. I suspect the South End was where they got the idea of Tele-Commuting in the first place. Sit home in your skivvies, listen to the Hi-Fi and make a living doing it.

But that isn't true either. When folks ask how I make my living, I say You call this Living? Truth be told—and it seldom is down at the South End—you got to be real creative to make ends meet. And more than that, you got to readjust your American

Values a mite or you're gonna feel Victimized instead of Queen-For-A-Day.

They say you can't buy happiness. You can't lease it either. Happiness takes work and sometimes I think you can't have two jobs in this world and you're going to have to pick. Lucky for us, here on the South End we don't have to make that choice.

Lost Highways

The South End has basically one main road, a two lane blacktop that loops around like a belt on a skinny fella. There's places where the old highway has fallen off the bluffs—you can still see pieces of the roadbed at the edge of Lefler's old place. Frank Lefler used to run the dump at the top of the hill where the Transfer Station is now. We call it a Transfer Station cause we don't keep our garbage any more. We transfer it.

Frank did too, really. About half what we threw away Frank brought home. Lefler's place was a veritable archeological site. He probably had the biggest middens since the Salish had theirs at Cama Beach. What took the natives a thousand years took Frank about 20.

I miss those days when we had a real dump. You'd go up and sit a spell with Frank, bring a few of his favorite beers—they were *all* his favorite—and he'd let you Forage thru the dump. All kinds of treasure then. They closed the dump back around '78, put these itty bitty dumpsters in where the Transfer Station is today and you'd put 75 cents in and the machine would close up tight and crush down your trash. Frank retired and went on to be the Fire Chief down at the South End. He finally burnt himself up smoking in bed in a trailer home they put him in on Dallman Road when his mind wasn't real focussed. He'd already sold his old homestead and I doubt the new folks know the Old Road is still running under their bluff... falling off in asphalt chunks... heading out to sea. I suspect Frank drives that road still on his way home from the dump. But then I always was a sentimental old fool...

Alternative Farming

They say Necessity is the Mother of Invention, but I say Poverty must be the Midwife. Down on the South End we have definitely seen our share of money making schemes. Folks have tried raising llama, they've tried fox farms, ostriches and alpacas, trout ponds, they've took a run at pheasants and my next door neighbor even tried quail. Quail of the Nile, he called em back in the sixties—gonna raise em and sell em in Hawaii. Fancy restaurants in Honolulu. Lulu is right. This old boy got liquored up one night and let loose about five thousand of these cute little quail and I tell you the coyotes fattened up for months until there wasn't a single one left. They couldn't walk up a gulley without their bellies dragging bottom.

I suppose the notion of a farm full of chickens and cows and pigs just wasn't exotic enough for the South Enders. Myself, I had peacocks for awhile, so I'm guilty too. I wouldn't be surprised if an orangutan ranch showed up at O-Zi-Ya someday.

Somewhere else, but not the South End, folks grow regular crops. Corn, peas, squash, tomatoes—tried and true. Down here in the Southern Latitudes, the farmers aren't what you might expect. I've seen magic mushroom herders, cannabis cowboys, organic produce ranchers, beehive wranglers, apple cider sodbusters, herbal homesteaders and flower franchisers. We must have something wrong with our well water is all I can figure. Some places have 'gentlemen farmers', we South Enders got nothing but Bi-Polar Farmers. It adds color to the area all right, but none of it green, if you fetch my meaning.

Inconvenience Store

Well sir, the South End is sort of like Hog Heaven to us that live here. We got Tyee Grocery, and that Art Gallery down there for entertainment. You can get everything you need at Tyee Grocery. You need a tomato, I don't care if it's mid-December, they got a tomato. Costs 95¢. You need a lemon in January, you bet. Costs 95¢. You want an onion in June. Yes sir, they got an old soggy, nasty looking onion. And you know what it costs…

I asked once why they don't just sell em by the pound like every other store in the world, and Dick, that's Dick Jr., Dick says, "Well, hell, cause we ain't got a scale."

So of course that explains the 95¢ apiece vegetables. Now coffee—and oh yeah, they got coffee—it costs $7.99 a pound. So being's how I'm sharper than the average booger on the South End I says to Big Dick one day, that's Dick Sr., I says, "Hey, Dick, if you haven't got a scale, how do you know how much my little pinch of coffee beans costs?" And Dick shows me on the bag where one pound is and a half a pound is and a quarter pound and my little piddle about one thirty-second of a pound so he charges me, yeah, 95¢. And I say, "what the hell, if I ground these beans up they'd be half up to where these whole beans are, so How About that?" And Dick says, "You want to buy them beans or don't cha?"

Now *that* is the point exactly. This isn't a 7-11. It isn't what you call exactly a Convenience Store either, sort of the opposite, really, but by god we're glad they're there, to save us that hellish commute to Elger Bay or the far-flung Plaza. You need milk, they got milk… one day before expiring. You want bread, they got the white kind… about two days from being croutons. And we don't eat croutons on the South End. Or Dijon mustard either, just the brand X French's kind. Which is what Tyee's got, thank you kindly…

Building Character

Now Elger Bay Store used to be an old house. It was a campground store mostly, catering to the park and folks from Cama Beach Resort hoping to get a better price than the Resort Store. Good luck. Old Lady Marcy ran the store when I came here. You wanted pop, you went on in the living room. You wanted a can of beans and franks, you went back in the bedroom. You wanted a loaf of Wonder Bread, you headed for the kitchen, you wanted a toy for the bored little brats stuck in the trailer for a weekend, you searched back in the dining hall. Most folks never found out what was in the bathroom. Truth is, it was the bathroom.

The Clarks bought the store about 1978 or so, bulldozed it down and built what you see now. We thought it was a damn 7-11. We ranted and raved and threw ourselves down on the ground. We cussed and spit and said we wouldn't shop there.

The Clarks would always get tourists who asked what was down the road on the South End, if it was worth the dangerous winding drive just to see the end of the island. Mrs. Clark would tell em, "Just a whole lot of nothing," and the tourists would hop back in their Volvo and head north. The Clarks probably kept the growth rate of the South End in check for more than a decade, God love em.

Course, progress can't be stopped and the Clarks sold to the Lanes and the Lanes sold to the Flickners and Elger Bay Store became the local Hot Spot this past quarter century. Funny how the years make things seem, well, historical. We were sad too when the Plaza got torn down, some ugly old box of a place sort of like the new Elger Bay Store which we thought had *character*. Character, these days, means it isn't part of a chain. If it's one thing the South End's got a ration of, it's character. There's about two under every rock.

Knuckleheads and Busted Knuckles

Just about everything you need is here on the South End. I admit we haven't got a MacDonald's yet and there isn't a Mall within hollering distance, but I'm talking about the Important Things, like a Modern Art Gallery, a café with friendly waitresses and a decent cup of joe, a mom and pop grocery that rents movies and knows your name, a little church to save a few souls—but not too many.

We used to have a garage and a junkyard back when Snowdens ran the store at Tyee. The first time I went to the garage, I needed my universal joints fixed. Ted was out there with his drinking buddy Seth—you see Seth Road by Mabana—that's who Seth was. They said sure, young feller, pull it right in, friendly as could be to a newcomer to the South End. I should've known things weren't quite up to snuff, though, when they had *me* under the truck handing *me* tools and telling *me* what to do next.

Course I was new and eager to get along with these fine neighbors of mine, and when in Rome, I thought, be a gladiator or be eaten. So with the help of these good ole boys I got the thing tore up right handily. Next day I hitchhiked into town and got myself some new universal joints—now I know you're thinking isn't it odd I got to go in myself, and I was thinking the same myself... but next night Seth and Ted drank and told lies to each other between supervising my cussing and grunting and smashing my knuckles and now I was thinking this is the damndest service station I ever had the misfortune to go to, but it was the *only* garage on the island and it got me out of the winter monsoon, so I kept at it.

When I got done and crawled out from under that greasy blood-spattered pit I'd spent hours in, I asked how much I owed em for my time. I mean they had a genuine Slicker here is what I figured. Ted said he thought maybe if I brought a bottle by someday, we'd call it even, and I thought well, that seems about fair.

It wasn't til a week later somebody told me Ted's wasn't a real Service Station—just a place he worked on his own rigs. Later, when I took the jug over, we had a good laugh at my expense. And that was the first and last time we had us a repair shop on the South End and near as I can tell I guess you're looking at the Head Mechanic. Retired now, thank you.

One Vote Landslide

I got a letter a few years back addressed to me, the Mayor of Camano Island. Now I know what you're gonna say, and I thought so too back then... one vote isn't gonna make me the Mayor of the South End, much less the Mayor of Camano.

The letter writer was petitioning me to do something in my Official Capacity, about a sign she didn't like on the highway, either *for* abortion killing babies or *against* abortion killing babies, and wouldn't I, as chief cook and bottle washer, take care of it?

I was flattered, of course. It's quite an honor being Hizzoner. But back then we had a Commissioner, Tom Shaugnessy, who actually lived on the Island. They all used to. Until this last fella who lives on an island 50 miles from me. In other words, he's abdicated the throne, if you follow my legal reasoning here.

So there's what we call in geo-political circles a Power Vacuum. A Power Vacuum with nobody to fill it. We all know from Florida that one vote makes all the difference, and ladies and gentlemen, it looks like I got that one vote...

So, you may be looking at the first Mayor of Camano. Maybe

the only one. I sure don't plan to have a recount and I don't see the need for stepping down. Course, now I better see about doing something about that sign. Keep my constituent happy. Don't want to ever lose that winning vote margin.

THE BIG DIG
ELGER BAY CANAL

UNSUCCESSFUL DIG OF 1910

SARATOGA TO PORT SUSAN

CREATING SOUTH END JOBS
PROVIDING WATERFRONT REAL ESTATE
SHIPPING ROUTES TO WHIDBEY ISLAND
BUILDING SOUTH END ISLAND
DIG IT NOW
DITCHES FOR HUMANITY

DADDLE DISTILLERIES

GREEN LIGHTNIN

100 PROOF
SINGLE LEAF
NETTLE MASH

SINCE PROHIBITION

ELGER BAY
INSTITUTE
OF
AESTHETIC ENLARGEMENT

EGO ENHANCEMENT WITHOUT CHEMICALS

EXPLORATIONS IN BIPOLARITY

SHRUNKEN ART FORMS REDISCOVERED

Enroll Today !!
1-800-ME-ARTIST

LOWER PAID STAFF MEANS LOWER TUITION

SOUTH END BLEND

JUMP START YOUR DAY

JITTER JAVA

COFFEE SO POTENT
THE UNITED NATIONS
NUCLEAR COMMISSION
HAS BANNED IT IN IRAN

34

A LIBRARY
IS NOT A BUILDING
IT'S A
UNIVERSE

LEARNING ...
THE CONTINUING EDUCATION

South End Literacy Foundation

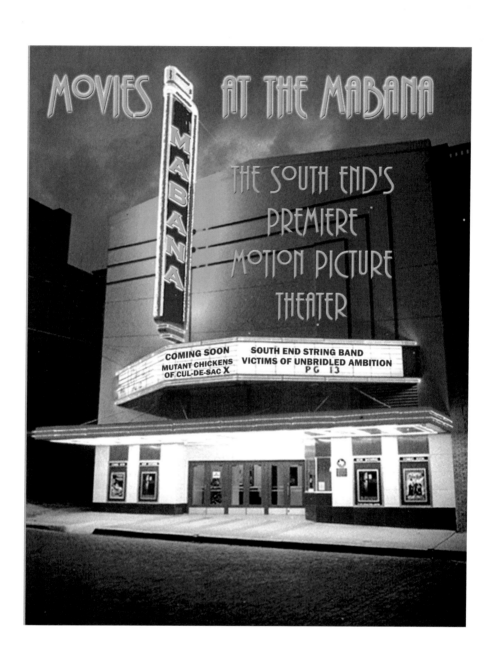

Gators in the Kiddie Pool

"From then on I decided to turn my back on a life of crime and to turn to a new and honest life. I went into the business of managing my own real estate and buying more real estate. Good luck to anyone who goes into the moonshine business. I might even buy a gallon or two".

Melvin Kivley, Stanwood moonshiner turned real estate developer. Busted by Federal Revenuers during Prohibition.

Down at the South End we ain't got jobs
The mizzus cries, the mizzus sobs

South End String Band

Ecological Armageddon

We got ourselves a population explosion down in the remote old growth nettle regions of the South End. Oh, I don't mean the realtors. They've always been breeding like rabbits on Viagra, but they eat their young which helps keep the numbers in check.

I'm talking about a fast growing, unchecked, immigrating subculture of brush-wielding, paint-pocked, ego-enhanced species we see proliferating like a red tide on steroids. I'm talking of course about the alarming influx of artists. Oil painters and glass fusers and watercolorists and auto salvage sculptors and photorealists and miniaturists and gigantilists and banner painters and stained glassers and raku potters and acrylic landscapists and Prozac escapists and mosaic tillers and woodworkers and glassblowers and egg tempura pointillists and fabric assemblagers—you name it, we got it or its going to be here faster than the bird flu. The Camano Art Association has 100 members. So does the Stanwood Arts Guild. The quilters do too. The waiting list at the Elger Bay School of Aesthetic Enlargement is backed up til the next decade. Our beaches are jammed with easels and our galleries can only show miniatures mostly.

At first we thought it was cute. Sort of quaint. Aunt Matilda painting tulips. Kinda like kid art on the refrigerator. Stick it up, praise the little tyke, tell him Picasso wasn't much better at age eight... But imagine the refrigerator with 16 layers. Then the stove. The wallpaper growing sediment. It's become a flesh eating collage that takes over the house, covers the barn, grows up the trees, clogs the power lines, spreads into the next county....

It's everywhere. *They're* everywhere. The grocery store lines with nothing but talk of the latest art show, the art gossip, the art meeting, the art gallery, the art, the art, my god, the art. Maybe it's too late. Maybe there's no cure. No biological control. No artist eating predators. The tide's already come in a foot higher from the weight of expanded egos. The climate has warmed from so much heated air. There may still be time... Unless of course the artists begin breeding with the realtors. Then, I think you know, we should all be very, very afraid.

Cannabis
Nudist Colony

We had another big pot bust down in the hollers of the South End recently. We got kind of a tradition down here on the South End of ignoring the prevailing rules and regulations. Used to run rum up and down the coast in the dark days of Prohibition. Some of the boys here decided to quit importing and took to distilling their *own* moonshine merlot. I confess to a little dabbling myself, just a bathtub batch occasionally to get through the winter monsoons.

We had a pot bust here a short time back that was a little different. Some old boy was up at the Pavillion movie theater multi-cinema complex in Stanwoodopolis, running past the Gunter murals nikkid as a jaybird. Down here we don't pay much attention to Idiosyncracy—other than to Celebrate it—but in Stanwoodopolis, you run around in your birthday suit, the Police are gonna blow out your candle for you.

Which they did. But in the course of their meticulous forensic work, the nikkid suspect admitted he might have tweaked his meds a mite too much and when the officers asked him where he got his prescription filled, he offered to take them right down to where he was growing it on the South End, *if* they would be kind enough to drive. And they were. So they did.

He showed em his fancy halogen growing lights and the fancy hydroponic watering system with the fancy electronic control mechanisms. His mizzus, when questioned, said she had *no* idea whatsoever what was out in that shed, just that he went out there to practice his Yo-Yo. I swear to God...

Now, I'm not gonna say we don't have some whackos and fruitcakes down here—after all, there's all these artists and I won't even bring up the musicians who breed down there in the ravines—but we're trying to project an image of the South End here that's something *north* of bohemian goofball rhapsody. And here comes this yo-yo—this Professional Yo-Yo—and it sets us right back to the pre-gated community days when we were all suspect.

So I hope come the next drug bust, you try to keep a perspective. And for the luvva Pete, you pot growers keep your pants on. We got reputations to protect.

Zen Mysteries

My brother doesn't live on the South End. Mama did her best, but I suspect her genes had just got tired blood or something, cause P.J. decided he wanted to Make Something of Himself and so he went a few grades beyond the School of Hard Knocks and got himself a law degree.

Some would say a Law Degree is nothing more and nothing less than a License to Steal. But I don't think that's an accurate appraisal, no sir. This country was founded on laws and I'm not one of these damn fools that blame the government for everything wrong with their lives. Down at the South End we just try to ignore such nonsense as best we can, and truth be told, we do right well at it.

My brother comes back every now and then. Sometimes on the porch late at night and the jug's near empty, he starts Philosophizing... He wonders if the folks down here on the South End come here cause they're strange already or whether something about the place makes em that way.

We've pondered on that many a long night and I tell you, it's about as useful as that chicken and egg debate. I just say you can't make an omelet with a hen and leave it at that. You think about the Hard Questions long enough and you might as well be a lawyer too. Like my old fishing partner used to say, "There ain't no mysteries for those who ask no questions…"

I wish I knew exactly what he meant by that, but I was always a little afraid to ask…

Disturbing Distilleries

Inquiring minds are always wanting to know how is it we South Enders never opened up a tavern or a bar? I have to tell em we're Virtuous folks and leave it at that... I guess the truth is we got a self-imposed Prohibition going on down here. Although I wouldn't say we was exactly *dry*. Desperate maybe, but not dry.

I got a friend up the road, she lives in a log cabin tucked in a grove of cedars and I guess those dark days of winter led to some lantern-lit research, cause by spring she was gathering nettles in big stinging batches and making herself a vat of nettle beer. You'd think it would taste god-awful. And you'd be right too—it was. She's still got the whole wretched vetch if you're interested. I'm sure it's medicinal and great for what ails you, anything that tastes that bad. Cheap too, I'm guessing.

I've made my share of bad liquor. Daisy wine—you won't find *that* in any recipe book. Fava bean wine. You'd shake so bad swallowing a dram glass of that you'd scare away diseases. I had a strawberry mead that was so explosive the FBI would take me for an al-Qaida terrorist now. I still got a spruce stout that'll take the edge right off those cold wet days of winter. Take rust off tools too.

My fiddling buddy Erich makes a fine merlot just so you know not all of us bootleggers have a reputation for blinding the neighbors with woody alcohol. Just most of us.

We're still experimenting. It's the South End Way. Gooeyduck beer. Salmon Cabernet. Fescue ale. Mussel Merlot. Rock Cod and Rye. I been trying to boil down sword ferns into something tantalizingly piquant, but the reviewers say I'd be better off drying em and smoking em. I said Hold On, that's a slippery slope. No telling *what* we'll be smoking on the South End next. We got enough problems as it is without backflashing to those terrible 60's. Don't you all worry, by next winter we'll have the fancy pants bars of La Conner using ferns for more than horticultural décor.

Custom Brick Outhouses

We hear rumors—even as far down as the South End—that the county wants to consider a sewer line. We haven't even got cable TV yet, but these government boys seem to want to pipe our waste to god knows where.

I got a lifetime of experience with waste management issues. The old outhouse still does a good job in emergencies, but it's practically a crime to own one. The cesspool was a real evolutionary step up on the South End—made indoor plumbing almost universal down here. For you city folks, a cesspool is exactly what it sounds like, but since it's covered over, it doesn't come with the aroma. Mine, of course, never *had* an aroma.

When I hear talk of sewer lines, what I hear are realtors and developers figuring out the How-To of stuffing more folks onto a postage stamp parcel. Water In/Waste Out. High rise condos. View townhouses. Pump the poop to Stanwoodopolis. They wouldn't know the difference. Do like Victoria B.C.—pump our privvies out to sea. Now there's a modern hi-tech waste management strategy.

Me and ma built ourselves a new palace awhile back and the

folks at the Health Department made it real clear they didn't want me doing the septic system myself. Boy, howdy, was the mizzus happy to hear that… But considering I framed the house, roofed it, sided it, plumbed it, electrified it, floored it, built cabinets and furniture for it, I thought I could probably handle the septic okay. Appears the county had its doubts.

So we paid an authorized septic specialist to dig us a big hole. And three trenches for the drain. Rocket science? Advanced degrees? If you had to build an outhouse today on the salty South End, the county would probably require NASA engineering certificates. And if you wanted a double seater, you'd better rent a Porta-Potty cause those permits are gonna take awhile longer.

Identity Crisis

Our island—the one the realtors like to advertise as 'the island you can drive to'—used to have a ferry way back when. More a barge really. Haul you and the farmwagon across the slough. Makes the Guemes Ferry look like a superliner cruise tour.

Our island—the one the realtors can drive to the bank—suffers from a sort of identity crisis. Are we really an island or are we just a glorified isthmus? A puny peninsula? Or worse, a stupid spit? An island has all those wonderful romantic connotations. Movie scene sunsets. Isolated beaches. Resort getaways. Fog-shrouded forests. Spinnakered sailboats and lonely lighthouses. Islands are places of mystery and intrigue. Pirates and rumrunners. Writers and artists and weavers of dreams. They don't make TV shows called Fantasy Isthmus. Paradise Peninsula. Sex and the Spit. Won't happen. Just doesn't set the imagination to tingling.

Whidbey suffers the same personality dilemma as Camano. Up in the San Juans, that cluster of isolated islands, that romantic archipelago, they exclude us. The San Juans. They won't let us in. They know something isn't quite right with us. They got a hundred *real* islands, even the ones that are nothing more than a barnacle covered rock. They let them in. Camano-Whidbey.

Sorry. Not a San Juan island. You ask me, it's archipelago apartheid.

We had to slink off and make our own county. Just so you know, just so you're real certain, we called it, in case anybody harbored any doubts, *Island County.* Not Isthmus County. Not Peninsula County. And sure as the tide comes up twice a day, not Spit County. But it doesn't help. We'll always be the islands you can drive to. Second class islands. Bipolar peninsula. Schizo Spit. Isthmus of the Insane. Some day the pharmaceutical conglomerates will find a remedy. Little purple pill, ask your ferry captain…

Cut-Throat Capitalism

Now I know most of you have heard the latest rumor—that Wal-Mart is thinking of moving into the Senior Center Thrift Store's location at the top of Land's Hill. Now you know and I know this is gonna split Camano Island right down the gullet.

Some folks'll say we already *got* cheap imported goods at the Thrift Store—why bring in a middle man? And some will say Wal-Mart will kill a way of life we've come to treasure here on the island. You know, commuting to Smokey Point for our supplies. If nothing else, a good excuse to dodge the chores...

The artists are already up in arms. As you know, artists are the Vanguard of Change, the Canary in the Strip Mall, the Little Light in the Refrigerator. They let you see what's coming before it clobbers you. Now this is all well and good, but I think there's been a misunderstanding. It's Wal-Mart—not Wall-*Art*. They're not selling cut-rate made-in-China original art to hang on the wall. The artists *still* got that market. We got to get the news to them before they start picketing or rioting.

Now you're gonna see a new Civil War. The South End against the North End. The old timers against the newcomers. The discount shoppers vs the boutique buyers. The expresso drinkers vs the drip drinkers. It'll be a bloodbath before it's settled. There's something *about* a Wal-Mart that sets off civil strife. Down at the South End we got pretty near all we need at Tyee Grocery. Costs a little more but sometimes you got to look a little deeper for the hidden costs of cheaper goods. That Wal-Mart might sell you a hammer half price, but if it's getting used on the neighbor, what's the ambulance bill?

We all like to pay less. Except maybe the Latte Lovers. But down in our depressed region we learned it's probably easier if you just learn to *buy* less. I know, it ain't the American Way, but maybe it would help minimize the social discord.

South End
Rifle Association

Now life on the South End isn't always a tranquil laid-back existence, despite my rose-colored descriptions. Every now and then a dark cloud passes over our perpetual picnic and we're reminded how fragile our blissful Garden of Eden really is.

The other night my neighbor's live-in girlfriend—I don't make judgements, I just assume it's a platonic companion on Easy Street here—well, she must've tweaked her meds a bit the wrong direction. Or else got fed up cooking and washing dishes. Or maybe just a combination of bad TV and career choices and boyfriend options. Whatever it was she decided it was time to chase my neighbor down the highway with his loaded gun.

We're used to gunplay on the South End. My other neighbor likes to shoot his shotguns up by the barn. Pellets rain down on me like raindrops. I usually call him up and ask as nice as I can to maybe aim it someplace else... Sometimes I suggest some places. If it's his thirty-ought-six, Ma and me head for the basement bunker. But we get alarmed seeing folks chasing each other down the highway with guns blazing. Something disconcerting about it. We believe in conflict resolution, but we draw a line. My neighbor's irate girlfriend was drawing a bead...

Well, pretty soon the phone calls brought the law. First a couple of county deputies, then a few more. Pretty soon 50 police cars in a nearby field. Three SWAT teams. Family counselors. The Stanwoodopolis News Crew. Curious neighbors. They closed the highway. The girlfriend holed up and threatened to kill *herself* when she couldn't kill her man, I'm guessing some made for TV movie plot she'd seen.

Course all's well that ends well. She surrendered by midnight. My neighbor's still alive. And the South End's back to its pastoral sleepy lifestyle. Although… I *did* notice some of us boys started storing the shooting irons where the missuz can't find em…

The Last of the SouthEndomish

We don't have many left, but if you search the old growth nettle forests, way back in the ravines, hidden from view in some fog shrouded bottomland where the sun rarely shines, you'll find em... Lichen covered, mossbacked old timers still speaking a native tongue foreign to most of us, with strange customs and wild fearsome looks.

I'm talking of course about aboriginal South Enders. The Original People. First Nation. Natives so primitive and xenophobic, few of us ever set eyes on them. Some folks never even heard *of* em, but you can sure hear em sometimes late at night when the wind blows cold from the firtops down into the backwash, a sound half human like a maniacal laugh two days after quitting lithium.

The missionaries we've sent in to convert em to our ways rarely come back out. The ones who do aren't the same. They tell garbled incoherent stories of all night parties, concoctions of mind-altering fungi, wicked good moonshine, half naked uninhibited dancing girls, banquets of exotic foodstuffs fit for the table of a Shah. And music, My God! The wild, mesmerising, hypnotic music. Drums and homemade fiddles and banjos made from sea lion skulls.

Some say these are the lost tribes of Paleolithic Stanwoodopolis who crossed the ice bridge to Camano Island and ended up trapped here when the glaciers retreated, leaving a local Galapagos. Some say these are really the artists. That they've infiltrated our modern culture, although obviously not quite getting it right. Some say these are the fingerpainters of dreams, the suburban Soul Catchers, the Banshees of the Baby Boomers.

There may be a little truth in *all* of that. Hard to say. But I'm glad they're back there. When the last of them finally goes the way of the dodo, when the night is filled *only* with the sound of late night talk show hosts telling jokes nobody half awake would laugh at, when the fescue has filled the ravines and the land is ruled by John Deere tractor-mowers, when everybody has horrible high paying jobs they hate at Boeing and the mythology of the South End is told by yahoos who vacation in Vegas, when the birdsongs have been drowned by electronic hum and the trails have all overgrown or been paved, when the wildness has been pushed back to make room for a world jammed with gadgets and junk we think we need and when time is measured no more by tide and moon, when the old ways are long since plowed under and the legends shrink shallow and days dry to puddles on a calendar, when our dreams are as dead as the buffalo and we know for certain we won't ever change the world… then it won't matter anymore who those people were or what their culture was or how they lived. The flintstroke that sparked the imagination to fire won't return. And what was once the South End will have made that final trek back to an origin we will never be able to follow. And this old homesteader will call it a day…

58

SINNERS
REPENT!
THE END IS NEAR
THE SOUTH END TENT REVIVAL

FUN FOR ALL

Bring the whole | **Damned family**

For a Bible thumping | **Rollicking good time**

STIGMATA WASH-OFF TATTOOS
GLOSSOLALIA CROSSWORDS | BRIMSTONE CHAINSAW ART
BIBLE ACTION FIGURES | SOUTH END PARABLES
BURNING BUSHES | WHITE SPIRITUALS

RAPTURE   RAFFLE

THE TRUTH REVEALED

REVEREND ROCCO "PAPA" LIPSE
PASTOR OF THE LITTLE CHAPEL
IN THE RAVINE

ADMISSION $6.66 ADULT
KIDS FREE
INFIDELS NO WAY

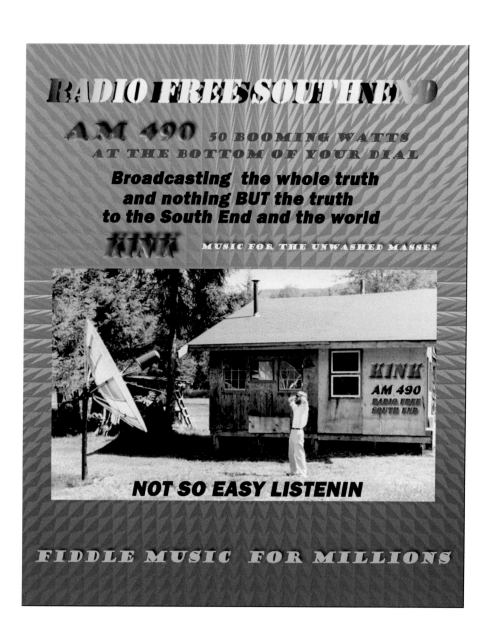

THE BAD BOYS OF BUILDING ARE BACK

PIRANHA
BROTHERS
CONSTRUCTION

"Permits? We don't need no stinkin permits!"

NO JOB TOO SMALL
NO BILL TOO HIGH

OVERNIGHT CONSTRUCTION OUR SPECIALTY

ILLEGAL STRUCTURES ON THE SOUTH END
SINCE 1979

61

SOUTH END
TRAILER TRASH TIMES
THE MONTHLY JOURNAL
FOR TODAY'S MOBILE MAN

FRONT PORCH BBQ TIPS
CHEF SWISH-KA-BOB
SHARES RECIPES FROM THE CAFE RETARDO

WORLD FAMOUS

SOUTH END

NETTLE FESTIVAL

A STINGIN GOOD TIME

NETTLE MAZE

AUG. 13, 14 AND 15

LABYRINTH OF ITCHING HORRORS

TURN BACK

WRONG WAY

UH-OH

LAST REMAINING

OLD GROWTH STAND

BRING THE KIDS
BUT CARRY A GPS

NETTLE LORE GALORE

NETTLE FABRIC ART

KIRBY'S NETTLE BEER

NETTLE CANDY

NETTLE PULL

SMOKED NETTLE

HEAVY NETTLE
ROCK BANDS

64

Free Range Clams: Political Correctness Unleashed

Freedom's just another word for nothing left to lose...

Kris Kristofferson

"So is poverty..."

Skeeter Daddle

Hate Mail

My father sends me political e-mails. Diatribes, really. Almost hate letters, if you want to know the truth. He's like most Americans. Get an e-mail joke, punch it out to 50 more recipients. It's like some voodoo chain letter curse. Break the chain and a Republican dies. I hope there's no Republicans reading this, cause I break the chain... so often I'm amazed Congress isn't 95% gay liberal pacifist Clinton-hugging weirdoes. Who want to give Al Qaida foreign aid.

But let's be fair here. I get e-mail from Bush Bashers too. Same poisonous feel. Same voodoo curse.

Down in the internet jungle, the rules are a little more, well, a little more... Oh, let's be honest. There are no rules. It's dog eat Hilary and cat eat Cheney. All etiquette is stripped away along with spelling and punctuation. Civilization seems a bit threadbare in the warfare of unvarnished words that fly like shrapnel on the web. It's as if gossip, the kind meant to inflict lasting psychic wounds, had replaced newspapers and journalism and reasoned inquiry as the source of record.

It's as if road rage was the new Voice of Reason. Or graffiti was the next editorial. Or a riot was our idea of public discourse.

I think it's time to turn down the volume. Turn off the venom. Tune to music instead of Hate Talk Radio. And whatever you do, *stop* forwarding those e-mail jokes. My old man has got to find something *else* to do with his retirement years...

Al-Qaeda Alpacas

Some of the boys' been lobbying to get the county to open up hunting season to us backwoodsmen. Buddha Bob, being a carrot killing vegetarian, he doesn't care, but the rest of these red meat eating carnivores here on the South End drive down the road every day and see those herds of overpopulated, long neck alpoodles overgrazing our shrinking farmlands and it gets em thinking... BBQ's. Shish-ka-llama. If Buddha Bob can eat Boca Burgers, we could surely eat Paca Burgers.

Oh, I know, they're about the cutest little fellas in the world. But deer aren't exactly ugly goobers. Rabbits aren't either. And we grill them up without too much squeamishness. You get to know my neighbors' cows, big moon-eyed, easy-going, mind their own cud creatures, you'd even think *they* were too cute to chew.

Now that the fishing's gone to hell and the crab season's shrunk down to near nothing and you even have to buy a license to pick seaweed, maybe this is the right time for a new harvest. Open up the season to us sportsmen. Thin the herds and fill the freezers too. I know, there'll be some negative publicity. Those liberal communist TV crews distorting our sport. Exaggerating the violence. The bloodshed. The suffering. Letters to the editor from Alpaca Huggers. Which is why we have got to stand united, stand resolute, get a good lobbyist. Appeal to our patriotism. Appeal to our fears.

There they are, wild herds of al-qaedas—I mean, al-pacas—furry, feral foreigners infiltrating our domestic livestock, our American livestock, and I think maybe it's time to ask the hard questions. Where are these things from? Who let em in? Do we trust em? What do they taste like? These things aren't *like* us. They're too dang cute, you ask me. They look at you wrong, all wide-eyed and smart, *too* smart, you ask me. These are dangerous times now. The enemy is everywhere. The enemy might be using these creatures. These creatures might be the enemy. All I'm saying is *this:* let's be careful. Hunting season might be just the answer…

Fishing Calculus

You folks who moved here in the last decade or so maybe don't know about the fishing we used to have. Fishing was really something awhile back. Salmon the size of Volkswagens. Salmon gangs cruising the beaches. Salmon highways up the rivers. Salmon spawning in the irrigation ditches, in the storm run-off, practically in the gutters. Dog salmon, pink salmon, king salmon, sockeye, chinook, humpies, tyee, silvers, blackmouth, so many salmon each one got three names, four descriptions and a different way of catching em.

Fishermen were as addicted to fishing as people are to gambling and drinking, which, I might note, are actually related diseases, although Fishing Anonymous hasn't really taken root despite the terrible toll fishing has taken on the social fabric of the South End. Fishing, you always hope to hit the jackpot on the salmon lottery. But no matter what, you can always drink. The bottle bass are always biting so the fishing's always good. Course, it's all part of the fishing pathology the scientific community never got around to studying.

You could stand on a beach in the heady heydays of angling and cast out for salmon from shore. You practically didn't need bait or lures or anything, just something to snag those big boys. But that wasn't how we fished then and it isn't how we fish now. We buy a boat first off. *Not* a rowboat… A fishing boat. Something that's big enough to handle some serious seas. Small is 16 foot. Better think bigger. You can't really think too big. Remember, you got gear and buddies, beer and gas tanks, poles, bait, life-jackets, fishfinders, GPS, ship-to-shore radios, coolers, giant tackle boxes, did I mention beer? You put a 50 horse motor on the back end, 50 at least, but, as always, bigger is better, and you strap a trolling motor on too, then a couple of Penn downrig-gers, battery powered, a big net and a gaff, double-check the beer supply, you're set to leave the dock. We're talking serious salmon fishing, mister. I know fellas who spend twice *over* on their fishing boats as they spent on their work trucks or the family car. But making sure that truck or car is big enough to pull the boat, that's priority One.

I knew a guy who had the math figured out for the mizzus. Old Don Mather, fished every morning before work, fished after work if he could, and for awhile—about when I worked for him as carpenter—decided just to fish all the time. Mathermatics. He'd pop a cold one and start figuring like this: two salmon a day times 365 days a year, that's over 700 salmon, oh round up, make it 800 times five pounds average each, but really probably more'n that, make it 10 pounds each, you got over four tons of salmon cost you $4.99 in the supermarket—pop another one—let's see, we're looking at, look out, we're into higher math now, he's got the pencil out and holy moly, $40,000 but probably more, being's how the price goes up all the time. And the bottom fish, figure maybe five pounds a day, ka-ching, ka-ching, and we got the clams too over by Ole's Cove, throw five or ten pounds a week on top of the fishing booty, ka-ching, ka-ching ka-zam, and the crabs, can't forget them, six a day limit on those Dungeness, hauling in 15 pounds a day at $3-$4 a pound minimum, pop another cold one, hit the cash register total and, well, Don was getting rich by *not* going to work, any fool could see that…

Me, I was going broke working for him because all we did was knock off early and head for the boat. And drinking all day long wasn't helping my bank account or my marriage no matter how many times I explained the math to *my* mizzus.

The real fishermen—the guys who talked, ate, breathed and bragged fishing 24/7—they hung out at the Stanwood Hotel. The Stanwood Hotel was Liar Central. They found out who caught what, where, using what bait, at what time of day, on what tide, drinking what beer. They dragged their monsters in to weigh on Mike's official scale and well, had a few more beers to take the edge off a hard day's fishing, then swapped tales of salmon so big they had to tow em behind the yacht and hope a bigger one didn't take it *and* the boat. Fishing was their *life*.

When the salmon started to dry up, so did some lives. The mathematics of the fishing boats started looking more and more like supply side economics with the supply side sprouting a stem to stern gash.

That way of life is nearly gone now. You see an angler or two gassing up the twin 150's at the Elger Bay pumps, geared for a day of trolling, but these are recreationalists, weekenders up from the suburbs looking for some hot action over by Baby Island, Fox Spit, Camano Head, the Greenbank Ridge, Ole's Cove, all legends now in a mythology of lost fishing lore... held in sacred keeping in the memories of men whose boats sit under tattered tarps on the South End, waiting for the salmon to return, one last great spawn up the mighty rivers.

Sleeping With the Past

My old shack's a fine old shack but every so often I'd get a Martha Stewart moment and decide to redecorate. Martha might not approve, but my preferred decorating tool was an old Homelite chainsaw. I wanted a little more light on those long winter days, well, sir, that Homelite was aptly named.

I found Ruby that way, cutting into the walls. I don't mean the mizzus. Ruby's this full size theater marquee from the 30's. Risqué, you might say. Got herself this skimpy little leather outfit on and not a trace of shy in eyes staring right at you. Old Lady Lathrop next door—her husband had the Quail of the Nile, but that's another story—she saw the poster and said, my gosh, that must be Ruby. She'd told me Ruby was a dancer, but somehow I guess I figured ballet or ballroom or something, not burlesque dancing, not stripping. But anyway Ruby lived in our house with her ma, Pearl, and Ruby and her husband built Old Lady Lathrop's place. Must've been just before World War Two, you know, the Good One.

Turns out there was a whole bevy of dancing girls who came up out of Seattle and Gomorrah to party on the South End. Artistic Eccentricity isn't anything new down here. My neighbors and me were rooting around in their ravine which had an old dump, digging for bottles and treasures, and by the end of the day we had 17 brass beds dug out, some as fancy as a cathouse and it made us scratch our heads why an old farm would have so many beds.

History is about half mystery, I always say, and I doubt we'll ever know why those beds were in that ravine or if my marquee is really Ruby. In the end, like a lot of what's been forgotten on the South End, it probably doesn't matter much and I don't lose much sleep over it in my brass bed with Ruby gazing beatifically down on me from where I hung her in the bedroom. Even the mizzus doesn't mind too much…

Family Values

Down in the foggy nettle ravines of the South End, we don't claim much moral high ground. We don't expect the neighbors to quit their church and join ours. We don't expect our family values got to be theirs. Truth is, we're just trying to live our lives as best we can, which is a full time job, and it doesn't leave much time to judge others.

A lot of folks these days apparently got plenty of time to cast stones. Not just us neighbors, the whole society. Not just the whole society, the entire world. Gone to hell in a handbasket, they claim. TV's the culprit. Hollywood. Advertisements. Drugs. Rock n' Roll. Sex. Sex? Hold on now, I tell em, that's a slippery slope. Get rid of that, goodbye family and forget the values.

All I can figure is anger must be a family value, right up there with righteous indignation. I say let's settle down. I sure didn't move to the South End to live with the local Taliban. Seems to me the whole point of immigrating to the South End, to the islands, to America back in 1620, was to be left the hell alone. Course, it *was* the Pilgrims who wanted the freedom to hang the witches...

It's easy to find witches these days. It's easy to find Evil. On the South End it's easy to find Sin. Not that I would know first-hand… What's hard is seeing it in ourselves. Thinking we're different. Thinking we can throw the first stone.

Freedom's a lot of things to a lot of folks. Especially these days. Definition's definitely shrinking, but keep this in mind: Real freedom's for everybody. Including the witches. Otherwise why'd the hell did we invent America?

Bubblegum Love Songs

On the slippery South End highway to love and marriage, we had to change our wedding vows a mite. That part about sticking together through thick and thin, better or worse, sickness or health, poverty or welfare, my god, it was like a prenuptial agreement for paupers. The mizzus sure wasn't too all fired happy about a 50-50 split on a leaky falling-down shack and a played out nettle farm.

We all grew up listening to those A.M. radio pop station Top 40 love songs. Bells banging away at First Sight. Beautiful people in purple polka dot bikinis. Love was a place where we were always gonna be happy with the perfect partner. Only death could do us part.

They say the French are the True Romantics. But I suspect us Americans are really the Love Crazed. I think that's okay. Maybe a bit unrealistic. Judging by the divorce rates.

Marriage on the South End is spozed to be a lifelong love affair. With the same person. What we end up learning is that marriage is really a partnership. That's a full time job. It's hard work. With ups and downs and sickness and health. You make it thru 50 years, you figured a lot of things out. That, or you have separate TV's in opposite ends of the house you watch too much...

I like to think it's the hard parts that bring us together the closest. The stuff they don't sing about on A.M. radio bubblegum love songs. The mortgage payments and the job layoffs and doctor bills and the price for nettle bales going down. When things looked the bleakest, the mizzus was there too, pulling hard.

It's why sometimes we look back fondly, us Old Timers, and smile at the memory of young kids, poor as churchmice, living in our shacks in Paradise on the slowly disappearing South End.

The Birthplace of E-coli

You all probably heard the rumors. A sea change is coming to the South End. A cosmic warp in the fabric of our sleepy unsusupecting rural existence. Nothing will be the way it was. No lives will go untouched. Mark my words: this will be the moment the Universe Changed for us South Enders.

No, they're *not* offering free dish TV. You still got to pay for ESPN.

I'm talking, of course, about Bartlett's Tyee Grocery selling. New owners. New management team. New marketing strategies. Maybe even new hot dogs on the electric rotisserie and buns that don't crumble into dust when you try to spoon in relish with the public plastic spoon that's breeding down in the 2 year old relish jar.

Some folks want Tyee to stay just the way it is. Outside privvy with the busted seat. Milk sold today as milk, tomorrow as cottage cheese. Vegetables priced individually. Each 95¢. All of em more wrinkled and tired looking than half the residents here. Some folks think Tyee is practically a museum of South End economics, a living tableau of Early Convenience Store and quite possibly the Birthplace of E-Coli.

No, we don't know what the future holds for the mercantile we've come to rely on for our everyday and emergency needs. We don't know what changes are in store at our favorite grocery store. But *one* thing's for sure in this crazy, mixed-up, uncertain world we live. At Tyee Store, you might not get what you want, you might not even get what you need, but if you do—and you can take this to the bank—it's gonna cost a little bit more.

Religion and State

We got ourselves a little chapel down at the South End. It's non-denominational, which means, I guess, they haven't got money either. Every Sunday they ring the bell they took from the old schoolhouse and call the flock to pasture. My cronies in the South End String Band don't attend real regular. Like most musicians, getting up by 10 a.m. isn't natural for them, but I notice most religions must feel like it's important to make hard working folks like us get out of bed early.

If I was a Preacher, I'd figure let the congregation sleep in, come on down when they're all rested up and alert. But it isn't my show and the church probably has got its own reasons.

You talk about separation of church and state, we used to vote at the chapel. Nobody seemed to care back then, but still, it isn't like we were Pilgrims, and finally some atheistic pinko commie liberal pervert must've took offense so we started voting down at the Fire Hall, more secular I guess.

We hear a lot of commotion from up north aways about prayer in schools and religion getting mixed into government and on and on, pretty heated up stuff. People take their religion fairly serious, I've noticed, and other people's they'd like to take some-where else.

I'm as religious as the next fella. I want to go to heaven but I'm not in any particular hurry to die, which makes me think deep down all of us are hedging our bets. Life's a gamble, but only a fool likes to draw to an inside straight...

The Theory
of Relativity

If you was to look at the South End on a map, it would look like a gooeyduck that had basked a little too long on the beach. Or like myself *before* the miracle of Viagra—if you catch my meaning... There just isn't a lot of blood flow down here.

I suppose that explains why the Pace of Life here is a little slower than other places. Stanwoodopolis has gotten so all-fired Accelerated—being a Hub and all—they finally had to install stoplights just to put the skids on a mite. I believe you could cram a whole afternoon on the South End into a Stanwoodopolis minute.

No, if it's one thing we got a bumper crop of, it's Time. Time on our hands, time on our shoes, time on our side. We watch the bread rise, the berries ripen, the orchards mature, the grass grow, the kids turn juvenile delinquent, the homebrew mellow, the hound dog and myself getting lazier with every passing year. What's that old chestnut about stopping to smell the roses...? On the South End we'd have to speed it up a few miles an hour.

You may not believe it, but Mr. Einstein must've had kinfolk on the South End cause he explained scientifically what we know in our bones down here—time is relative. Hell fire, I had a shirt-tail cousin come to visit Ma and me awhile back, brought the whole kit and kaboodle, dogs, brats, teetotaling wife, stayed a week. I'm telling you when that week was over, me and the mizzus was two *years* closer to the Pioneer Cemetery.

People say Mr. Einstein was a genius. I say he probably just had himself some questionable relatives.

Porch Gridlock

In the backwoods of the South End we're still a Hunting-Gathering society. I don't mean squirrel hunting and nut gathering. I'm talking about bargain hunting and garage sailing. Jump in the jalopy Friday and Saturday morning, head north in search of treasure.

The emigrants who moved here a year ago thinking they'd found Hawaii and are selling out now thinking they're leaving Iceland—they're piling the yard with their castoffs the way the pioneers lightened the load of their Conestogas. Get rid of it and Good Riddance.

We live in a glut of consumerism here in the richest country in the whole world. The stuff we throw away would be a high end department store in Sudan. I always wondered why the retirees who come here, just them and the mizzus, build a home with four bedrooms, six baths, two dining rooms and a theater. So they can store the stuff they buy, is why. Down by us, these days the garages are bigger'n my house. Got to be to get the boat and the trailer, the RV and three cars and the lawn tractor and the motorcycles and the antique car restoration project and the mountain bikes and the kayak and the overflow of stuff from the

3,000 sq. ft. home they built that's nowhere big enough now.

So a garage sale to us South Enders is like going to Sears Roebuck. Saves us a long drive to the mall… and the salespeople are friendlier. "You like that lawnmower? Here, I'll throw in a dinette set and the wife's Camry. Give me a buck, we'll call it good. Fifty cents more, you can have the color TV too."

The trouble is, of course, *our* porches are filling up at an alarming rate. Which explains the proliferation of storage units in the area. Packrats like South Enders never have garage sales. Maybe we should…

Hizzoner, de Mayor

Used to be we kept a giant billboard at the bottom of Land's Hill coming onto the island telling any and all that this was Private Property. The beaches, the clams, the crabs, the whole shebang were owned by us property holders and if you knew what was good for you, you'd stay off our land.

This was about 1980 and some old boys from the Camano Homeowners Association decided to erect the thing. Stanwoodopolis has a Wellkommen. Camano had a *Keep Out...* Somebody cut it down right off the Get-Go. I thought about doing it myself, it was so nasty and in your face. But it got put right back up with steel legs hidden inside the wood ones so a chain saw wouldn't work to take it down next try.

Being on state highway right-of-way, the sign was illegal. A few years later another sign went on the big sign covering up the Keep Off Private Property with a Respect Private Property at the bottom. Not near as hostile, but still not real inviting. Twenty years that sign sat there guarding the island's only entry by would-be trespassers.

About 1998 we were building the new Visitor Center at Terry's

Corner. Department of Transportation came by wanting permission to tear that sign down. Wanted to know who put it up, who owned it, who maintained it. Me being at the corner every day, they figured I must be the head honcho of the Chamber of Commerce. For two years I got calls from D.O.T. wanting to cut me a deal. They'd put the sign up at the Center for us. I said with a sign like that we wouldn't *need* a Visitor Center. Just tear the ugly thing down. Nobody's alive who cares. But they were worried about stepping on toes. I said those old boys sure didn't care whose toes they stomped on when they E-rected that thing.

D.O.T. kept calling. Like I'm the Mayor of Camano. They'd put fancy stripes in our parking lot if they could tear it down, the man said. Finally I said, okay, you got a deal. And that's how we got rid of that ugly sign and how we got fancy stripes too. Personally I wish I'd cut a deal now to put that sign up at the entrance to the South End. Plus they'd have had to make me honorary mayor.

Party Line Misnomer

Time was when the South End backwashes were undiscovered by the modern world. We were so remote even the real estate agents hadn't parceled us up and sold us off as tropical getaways. We were like Amazonian tribesmen with bones in our noses living where not even cable TV could gouge us.

Now, of course, we got satellite Dish TV reception and our kids got nose piercings. Civilization works in mysterious ways…

Used to be Ma and me were connected to the rest of the world by party line. Phone Company wanted a dollar a mile a month from office headquarters in Mt. Vernon to our shack to get a private line. So we shared our access to the outside world for years with a single mom and her teenage daughter. Meaning, we totally lost communication with civilization. Might as well have thrown that rotary telephone in the woods for all we got to use the line…

Times have changed. Ma and me got his and her computers now. We don't have to machete a path through the jungle to get our news anymore—we just Google up anything you can imagine, get what we need in about two nanoseconds. Course, I share the line with Ma now. Which makes me pine for the days of Mrs. Chats-for-all-she's-worth and her teenage daughter. I been thinking of throwing my PC next to the rotary phone back of the outhouse. Either that or pony up the money for a second line. Maybe times *don't* change as much as we think…

The Last Peacock Migration

I used to raise peacocks. You ever seen peacocks strutting through a South End shack yard, it's sort of otherworldly. They brought an elegance that's indescribable to my backwash palace. You ever *heard* one of these exotic creatures, you might reconsider classing up the bottom land. They got a scream like a child being tortured. I guarantee the neighbors will wear out 911 with their calls of mayhem and madness at your place.

Course when I had the peacocks, we didn't have neighbors. No, they didn't move away because of the noise, they just hadn't Discovered the fabulous South End yet.

My peacocks, no offense to any of you Bird Huggers—my peacocks had a head about the size of a big martini olive. And inside that head they had a brain the size of, well, a pea. My peacocks were not bright. They made a chicken look like Albert Einstein. They thought my Banty hen, who'd hatched their eggs, they thought she was not only Einstein, but their mama and God too.

Don't ask me what I was thinking. My brain isn't real big either. Although I'm pretty sure who my mama is but don't ask me about Pop. I'm like the peacocks—I just go on faith.

I had the peacocks a few years until Mama Banty got picked off by a Wily Coyote. They wouldn't come back to the henhouse after that, so they roosted in the cedars every night. Dumb or not, they figured out the climbing ability of a coyote. Finally they decided to go looking for Ma. The Police Blotter in the Stanwood Gazette—and this is the Gospel Truth—would report on their progress north. Peacock sighting at Dallman Road. Peacocks seen gathering at Sunnyshore. Eventually they found a chicken surrogate ma up by O-Zi-Ya. O-Zi-Ya is Southend-omish, meaning, I think, Ornithological Orphanage.

Sometimes I miss those little pea-brains. Although I can sleep longer without an alarm clock that sounds like a nightmare. I wonder, though, if I'd kept em, if the South End might've stayed, oh, I don't know, less developed. Maybe forced the new neighbors to move north instead.

SOUTH END GYPPO

REAL MEN CLEARCUT

LOGGING
the old-fashioned way...
with extreme prejudice

PHOTO OF LAST SPAR AND DONKEY OPERATION
MUSEUM OF THE SOUTH END SUBURBS

95

WINDY REAR REALTY

"MORTGAGING DREAMS IS OUR BUSINESS"

AIN'T GOT A POT TO PEE IN?

**NO PROBLEM ...
OUR EXPERIENCED STAFF
HAS THE RIGHT HOME
AT THE RIGHT PRICE**

SOUTH END
SATELLITE
COMMUNICATION

SOUTH END STORAGE

Just cause you live on the South End
Don't mean you have to live like trash...

Front porch backin up?
We still got room!

"Savin marriages since 1957"

100

Suburbanites
at the Gate:
Backhoe Archeology

*There was madness in any direction, at any hour. You could
strike sparks anywhere. We had all the momentum; we were
riding the crest of a high and beautiful wave... So now... you
can go up on a steep hill... and with the right kind of eyes you
can almost see the high-water mark—that place where the wave
finally broke and rolled back.*

Hunter S. Thompson

*But I'm near the end and I just ain't got the time
And I'm wasted and I can't find my way home.*

Steve Winwood

Bubba's Outhouse
Service & Repair

Plenty of the newcomers to the South End often times find themselves in need of experienced pioneers to help them fix their dilapidated wells or rotted porches or falling down barns. They let their fingers do the walking, call a few local good ole boys in the Yellow Pages, figuring they'll hire some poor, hungry, hopefully desperate South Ender to work that afternoon or tomorrow fixing up their homestead so the mizzus'll quit crying.

They get a recorded message, you know: "This is Bubba's Outhouse Service and Repair. I'm out on an emergency call right this moment, but if you all would leave your name and number, I'll get back to you soon as I'm done fixing this city slicker's plumbing dilemma…"

They expect he'll call right back. They expect he'll call tonight at the latest. They expect he'll call back by tomorrow at the very latest. What they don't expect is what us South Enders refer to as South End Entrepreneurial Ennui… more commonly known as Who Gives a Damn? Not these boys, that's for sure. They might call back in a couple of weeks. But don't bet on it. Folks ask me, are they uppity? Are they busy? Don't they like newcomers? Are they too dumb to figure out the fancy answering machine?

I tell em yes, and leave it at that.

Truth is, they're like the rest of my buddies down here, sort of permanently semi-retired. Work isn't exactly a priority until their money's gone. So if you find yourself in need of a handyman, good luck to you. Won't be long til you figure out why most of us have to fix everything ourselves. That, or do like me, just let it stay broke and quit worrying about it.

Plant Swapping

My neighbors across the road, every year now, put iris bulbs out on the highway with a sign that says *free*. Cars stop, trunks fly open and another load of plants migrates south. Over a hundred varieties of irises they brought from Oklahoma are taking over the South End, iris capital of the world.

This is a new twist on an old country tradition—passing plants to the neighbors. Look around and you'll see our quince bush is about the age of the Nesje's up the road. There are three sequoias in the neighborhood, all about the same height and age. Our mock orange is showing up from here to Tyee.

A cutting here, a few bulbs there, a piece of honeysuckle vine, a funny vegetable like our Jerusalem artichoke, some plants that made a jail break on their own like our comfrey, trees like my neighbor's chestnuts that pop up everywhere or our filberts the blue jays plant for us and everybody else—the plants get spread around.

The mizzus is a horticulturist. Me, I'm more of a hortichuckle-ist. I used to find plants back in the hollows, at old homesteads, by hidden ponds and muddy creek sides. I got one, a 7-foot tall monster wild orchid, a Jumpin Jimmy that spreads by spitting its seeds out of a pod. We'd find em on the roof, up in the gutter where the mulch is about a foot deep, nearly everywhere but in the house... at least for now.

You got to be careful, I guess. I suppose it won't be long before the moralists take a swing at this. Plant swapping. It isn't natural. It isn't right. Ought to nip it in the bud. Stick to the native plants. Live on stinging nettle soup and quit importing foreign vegetables. Send those potatoes back to Ireland and those artichokes back to Israel where they belong...

Personally—and don't tell Ma I said this—I'm all *for* plant swapping. Seems neighborly somehow. And saves me from those collecting trips back in the jungle and the swamps now that the Jumpin Jimmies have taken over everything in sight.

Mt. Mole

A lot of folks come to the country and are surprised by the surplus of pests they didn't expect. Bald eagles snatching the Pekinese off the porch. Otters snacking on their $2,000 pedigree koi. The same otters leaving the leftovers under the house where the rotten carcass of carp would gag about anybody *but* an otter. The coyotes eat the cat, the cat eats the birds, the birds eat the cherries. The deer eat the prized roses and my neighbor behind me—a two legged pest—poaches the deer and the occasional stray dog that shows up too. A lot of gunplay out in *my* neck of the suburbs.

My neighbors think the garbage eating, begging raccoons are cute as buttons. They feed em dog food like they were pets. The possums don't seem so cute somehow. Pointy snouts, hairless, tumorous, sharp little teeth. Somehow less than cuddlesome. A few years back we had cougars. Two hundred pound cats. Jump a 6-foot fence with a lamb wiggling it its jaws like paragliding in a breeze. Easy for a mom to picture little Jimmy instead. Remind you real quick that the country isn't *only* golf courses and weed n feed lawns.

But the scourge of the suburbs, the menace of the manicured

fescue, the *real* threat to Easy Living, is the wily mole. Burrows up every night through green perfection and you best believe a mole hill to my neighbors *is* a mountain. They shoot at the burrows, dump gasoline and poison into the holes, blow em up, toxify em, trap em, sonic noise em, drown em, irradiate em and eventually just stand back and curse em.

The moles will, in the last great showdown as the sun sets over the sprinkler showered suburbs, the moles will ultimately *win*. I suspect the tunnels all connect in one vast freeway system and their complex civilization has cities and art and language and calendars far beyond our meager comprehension. We're their slaves, keeping the gardens tilled, the lawns watered, their elaborate canals flowing. And the beauty of it is, we don't suspect a thing.

Underground
Stanwood

The South End, as always, is way out front on the region's transportation issues. Take the Elger Bay Canal, a.k.a., the Big Dig. Fifty years ago we were advocating a series of locks and dams to connect Port Susan with Saratoga Passage, open up shipping through the South End—South End Island, I might add—to the Mainland from Langley, Greenbank and Coupeville. Sure, it would've been costly, but in 1950 dollars, about what a building lot costs in Finnistere now.

But just because nobody listened to us *then* doesn't mean we aren't talking *now*. One thing about a South Ender, we don't wait for an audience. Today we have what some see as a problem— and the South End sees as an opportunity—at the Mark Clark Bottleneck Bridge. Two lanes squeezing through the Sewage Flats of Stanwood, all cramming onto the Mark Clark, a 50's bridge named after a WW2 general who almost, but not quite, lived here. If he'd cut a wider swath in the war, maybe we'd have built a wider bridge.

The South End Greater Metropolitan Economic Council (SEGMUCK) has not only a vision, but the solution. A tunnel, ladies and gentlemen, six lanes *under* not only the Stillaguamish, but under all of Stanwoodopolis. Out of sight, out of mind. A win-win for the Camano commuter sick of big box grocery chains, dying strip malls, bad signage and the Twin City Foods Concrete Curtain. Sure it's an engineering challenge. Sure it costs more. But in 2050 dollars probably what an apartment costs in Camano Condos.

Call Mary Margaret down in Olympia. Let's grab that Seattle Viaduct money while they're busy squabbling. It's a once in a lifetime opportunity. Don't make the mistake of the Elger Bay Canal. Let's build the Stanwood Bypass. Together we can dig our way home!

Fair Winds

We all got our reasons for coming to the islands. Some of em romantic. Some of em practical. Some of em driven maybe by desperation. Some of us came in search of elusive dreams, of ephemeral beauty, of something as prosaic as sunlight sparkling against the cold steel heart of Puget Sound waters. Some of us sought a refuge. From the past, from the banality of former jobs, from a world that demanded too much of us... so much we feared losing ourselves completely. Some of us came on a search. For a new world. For another chance. For impossibilities not yet imagined.

We all came for different reasons to a place where America ends, where the waters separate us from the continent and from each other, where we may have wondered if we'd reached some last frontier in our lives and there was only Making Do or Admitting Defeat and Going Back.

I guess it's fair to say all of us here didn't go back. I know, though, there are days when the winds blow the past through the boughs of my life like rocking a cradle of remembered dreams, where I feel the old tug of solid land and the serenity of occupations and the consistency of a calendar. That wind whispers what might have been and what was lost and who was missing, all the regrets and doubts and reminiscences.

But the pull of the wind isn't *that* really, isn't that at all. It's something at the edge of a lapping tide just beyond a stand of ancient fir sentinels, something distinctly familiar that we don't recognize quite yet. Something known but not yet named. Something immanent but not yet born. Something that we're going to create ourselves. That will set our sails to a wind that we will soar on as far as our imaginations can take us.

That's why we came to these islands. And on that breath that creates us is the only way we'll leave...

South End Signpost

People ask all the time: where *is* this South End you keep talking about? Does it have its own Zip Code? Do you have to cross a bridge, take a ferry, pay a toll? Is it a Real Place or sort of *Look... up ahead... what's that signpost?*

Maybe the South End of the Twilight Zone, Rod Serling as ghostly mayor? Can anybody go there or do you need a doctor's prescription?

A roadmap of the South End is what they want, maybe a four color tri-fold brochure they can get at the South End Chamber of Commerce building that's temporarily installed in the trailer next to the Windy Rear Real Estate Office. Trouble is, the staffing at the Visitor Center's been real spotty since Jolene found a full time position at the new Wal-Mart Superstore 40 miles away. And the County's been less than happy about health concerns with the Chamber's lack of restroom facilities... which gives fresh meaning to the idea of Chamber Pot.

No, the South End is half metaphor and a third allegory and over a quarter geographically fantastic. For those who live there, it requires an imaginative Vigilance just to keep oriented. For those who visit, at least the Literalists, it must be a constant Slippery Slope that leads to a beach where the road ends and the tide is coming up real fast.

I've lived on the South End most of my adult life, which is not very long, maybe a few days Total. So I can't tell you exactly where the South End *is*. But if you need a map, I don't think you'd really want to go there. You'd load up the kids, pack the SUV, throw on some bikes and camping gear, make reservations and drive half the damn day across some synapse with a half built bridge. The kids would be crying, the mizzus would want you to *keep* asking directions and by nightfall you'd see the gas gauge reading empty and no stations anywhere. The South End, you see, isn't a Destination. It's really the place you start *from*.

Downsizing the American Dream

Down here in the harsh environment of the South End, we're always struggling harder than most to climb the ladder of success toward *middleclasssdom*. In America we've lowered our sights. *Course* we all want to be Bill Gates or Donald Trump or Michael Jordan, but in the end, we gauge success by the size of our SUV and our HDTV and our credit card debt limit. Some might call this downsizing the American Dream. On the South End we call it Super-Sizing the Happy Meal.

Used to be we valued innovation, creativity, risk-taking. Now we're content if we can keep our boring job and make the payment on the Humvee. Once upon a time in the West we measured success by what we *did*, not what we owed. We judged a person on grit and determination, not on the size of their pension package.

Nowadays in the Land of the Free and the Home of the Brave, we're just trying to hang onto what we used to never want. Low maintenance yard. Low maintenance chateau. Low maintenance lifestyle. Low maintenance dreams. A humdrum grey world of reruns, old movies on new DVD's, easy to fix meals, oven ready, dishwasher safe, no money down, easy financing, give me a break, pull up the sheet and tell me good night...

I'm sorry. That isn't good enough on the salty South End. Not for hard bit characters who came here to escape the easy living advertised on cable TV. Life is something you *make*, not buy. Life is something you create, not use credit for. Life is something you work on, not retire into. The old American Dream of guts and calluses and an imagination big as a frontier might seem out of reach to most people these days, but on the South End it's the Real Deal. And you can forget about extra fries or a 32 oz. drink...

School of Hard Knocks

Most of my neighbors are retired fellas. Like myself. They got a travel trailer, a big screen TV, titanium golf clubs and a nice pension. Me, all I got was a beat up hat... Course, I didn't work 50 years either so I guess it's only fair.

Retirement, for you poor folks who still work, is supposed to be a kind of halfway house to heaven. It's a chance to get used to boredom, bad TV and lawnmowing. The grass across the highway from me is immaculately green from chemical fertilizers and chemical weedkillers. My poor dandelions wouldn't stand a chance over there.

In heaven somebody else must mow the grass with real quiet John Deere mowers. In the halfway house of retirement, the mowing goes on 24/7. It's how you beat the boredom. Some of these boys mow three times a week. I suspect the wives inside the palaces are doing all the dishes two or three times every meal too.

Some folks handle retirement better than others. It's like the South End, sort of a state of mind. I try to be a Role Model for these fellas, sit up on the porch, my pension pulled down low over my eyes to keep the UV off my delicate skin, and wile away a lazy afternoon with some ice-cold homemade beverages and a 5-string banjo keeping time to the mowers.

Course everybody only hears what they got ears to hear. You can bring a horse to water but you can't necessarily give him a bath. My neighbors got plenty of time to learn from me. After all, I been retired most of my adult life. Problem is, free advice, they figure, is worth what it costs. I bet if I started night classes, charged tuition fees and sold my homebrew by the glass, they'd line up at the Camano College of Hard Knocks by the drove. Might even shut off the lawnmower for awhile…

Career Counseling

Down at the South end, Outsourcing isn't anything new. We been sending our jobs somewhere else practically since they built the Mark Clark Bridge. Been sending our people looking for em too. We don't know if they found those exported jobs or not... nobody ever came back to report.

The great Industrial Engine that *was* the South End is gone now. Replaced by service jobs. Three of em, at the Tyee Grocery. Minimum wage. No health care. No benefits, unless you count all the hot dogs you care to swipe from the electric rotisserie deli. Which'll be offset, as I said before, by lack of adequate health care from the onset of food poisoning...

I suppose America can use the South End as its model and its inspiration. Ironically we'll probably achieve full employment when whole platoons of South Enders become $1,000 a day consultants for government think tanks and corporate task forces desperate to quiet a population sick of working with their teenage daughters at the burger joint. Family values might not work as a catch phrase *this* time.

The SOL—South End Outsourcing Liaisons—will serve as

beacon and light to a troubled economy. Being patriots, it's the least we can do. And $1,000 a day is the least we'll take. Our message is a simple message, even if its execution is hard. But it's a proven prescription. Tested by porch rockers here most of their non-working lives. Scrutinized, I hasten to add, by the IRS auditors year after year. We know it works. We know it's legal. And we know America needs it.

Our advice—to you folks in simple layman's terms cause you aren't paying for the big consulting fees for the convoluted explanations—our advice is this, in a nutcase: *Retire*. Quit. Give up. Then become a musician. An artist. A writer. Stop your worrying. We did. And we aren't starving. Course if you see us at the Tyee Deli with one of those day old dogs in a crusty bun, best reconsider.

Backwash
Bureaucracy

Volunteerism wasn't *invented* on the South End, but like a lot of places far from the reach of Rome, the empire isn't gonna be much help. In modern times we like to moan and whine and blame the government for this and blame the government for that. President Reagan said the government *was* the problem. I hate to kick a fella when he's down, especially six feet, but I think if you're president of the most powerful country on the face of the planet, commander-in-chief of the universe's largest army, head CEO of the galaxy's biggest bureaucracy and you think the problem is government... Well, that's like Bill Gates wishing he didn't have to hassle with filthy money. You believe that, dead or not, you'll vote the Gipper back for another term.

Government makes a fine punching bag. Especially for satirists and malcontents and lately Presidents of the United States. Down on the South End we might get an assessor sniffing around every four years or so, checking for tax roll purposes to see if we put a concrete foundation under the outhouse, but mostly we're left to our own devices. On the South End, believe me, de vices rule...

Down here we need something done, we don't call up the county anymore. We Know they haven't got the personnel, we Know they haven't got the money, we Know they never heard of Camano Island, much less the South End. We just suck it up and go do it our damn selves. Used to be a time in America when this is how we *expected* to do things. Used to be we *liked* it that way. "Self reliance," Ralph Emerson called it. "Can-do," Teddy Roosevelt said. "Thousand points of light," the first George told us. "Zip it up," Clinton admonished. If the adage that those who govern least govern best, our county government's doing a great job.

Palma Non Sin Pulvere

I can't drive off the South End without running into promotional prizes, free offers, gambling gimmicks, raffle drawings, goofy give-aways, you name it... Sign up for this, they'll give you that for nothing. Buy this, they'll give you that too. Everybody seems to think this is just the Way of the World. That we oughta get something for doing nothing. Even if the something is a piece of useless junk.

They got frequent flyer miles and rebates and coupons and accumulating credit on your Mastercard. They got gifts if you sign up today, they got a valuable prize if you join by the end of the month. They'll give you a trip to Las Vegas if you'll listen to a sales pitch.

I come from another planet evidently. My family has a coat-of-arms from back when they were a clan back in the hollers of Scotland. We don't do that so much anymore. Mine even had a motto: Palma Non Sine Pulvere. Latin, in case you thought the ancestors were a little feeble on the English. It means No Money Without Work.

My ancestors must've been looking way down the road to come

up with that cherry. Before games shows and lotteries and reality TV and casinoes and offers in the mail every damn day for free money. When they thought up those words of wisdom they were proud enough to put on the family emblem, I seriously doubt anybody offered em free stuff because they were good looking. Good safe bet, I figure. Hell no, I won't take a handout. No sir. My family's got its pride, m'lord. Next thing you know we'll be on the welfare lines. Slippery slope, that, Squire.

I suppose if the patriarchs and matriarchs of my clan assembled today to update the family slogan, they'd probably change it. Something more modern, more in keeping with the times. I was thinking maybe Foolicus Damnicus Pulvere. Work is for Damn Fools.

A Gated Garden of Eden

Some folks who come to the South End see the new houses, the suburban style developments with names like Shannaron or West Shores or Tillacum, Eagle Ridge, Port Susan Terrace, they think, oh, what a charming seaside community. My favorite is the Preserve. Preserving the developer's bank account maybe. Not much else.

But nobody should expect things to stay the way they want. It isn't the way of the world. Things change and that's something you can take to *your* bank. The South End's changing too. We can tell you cute stories of shack life and tales of trailer glory. Thrill you with the bygone days. Make you smile at our mishaps.

The truth is the South End was poor. The way a lot of rural, backwash America is poor. Land was dirt cheap. The houses were rundown, neglected, often times abandoned. This was a place where people came to vacation, not to live. What was cute in July wasn't so charming in dismal December.

Back not too many years you didn't have many families living here—you had retirees like myself. Work was too far. People, sensible people anyway, wouldn't consider driving two hours one way back then. Now they practically *live* in their car. I think this is why Rush Limbaugh is so popular. He's got a captive audience that's mad as the devil, stuck in traffic, hating the whole crazy world that somebody, but not *them*, made a sorry mess of.

Life *was* different down here. You think these stories are exaggerated, you'd be wrong. It was like going back in time. Folks lived closer to the ground… if you catch my meaning. Fishing, crabbing, clamming, hunting—not for sport. For food. You see more flower gardens at my place now, but in the early years, the garden grew mostly vegetables.

I bring neighbors and visitors into my studio. My 'studio' is our old shack. Lived there from '77 to '94, I tell em. Seventeen years. The studio is quaint. Charming in a rustic, dirty kind of way. But the idea of human beings living in it, much less living in it 17 years, you can see in their response it's not a pretty picture. The living *was* hard. But you lived in the wildest, most beautiful place you ever imagined. You got to homestead at the end of the 20th Century. And you found something here you might never find again.

A simplicity. A harmony with the land and the weather. A quiet rhythm to your life. An acceptance of life as a worthwhile struggle. And a deep and abiding love of the South End.

You want to know the reason we tell these stories—I guess that's the reason…

Linguistics

They say the Eskimos have 50 words for snow. Down at the equatorial jungles of the South End we got more than that describing rain. We even got words for when it *doesn't* rain: Partly Cloudy. Dripping. Chance of Showers.

Folks who visit ask does it rain here all the time? And I say, depends on what kind you mean. You talking downpour or drizzle? You referring to sprinkles or showers? Gullywashers or mist? Thunderstorms or real heavy drippy fog? Intermittent or steady? Rain mixed with sleet? Rain mixed with snow? Rain mixed with tears?

I suppose we're splitting hairs. It's all soggy, moldy stuff. People are surprised when we tell em the average rainfall on the South End is less than 24 inches a year. Rainshadow, I tell em. Like living under a wide-brimmed hat. Not exactly dry but it explains why most of us don't own umbrellas.

Some folks can't take it. They pack up the show about November and head for the trailer park luxury of suburbs springing up in Nevada, New Mexico or Arizona. Isn't any word at *all* for rain down there. Rainbirds, we call em on the South End. Set up in some pleasant desert cul-de-sac and snicker at us mossy coots they left behind under the dripping evergreens.

Around April or May they'll come back to air out the mildewed shack. Won't be a week before they're adding to the rich vocabulary we got for wet precipitation. Mostly four letter ones.

Rural Incineration

Folks move out to the South End and right off, they got notions how you might live in the country. First thing you need, they think, is a Burn Barrel. Garbage pick-up's spotty so why not go out back, prop up a 55 gallon metal barrel with the top off and burn anything that will... plastic bags, plastic bottles, yesterday's newspaper ads, the construction left-overs, treated lumber, aluminum cans, asphalt roofing, old telephone books, old telephones.

You can get a lot into a Burn Barrel. Course, it mostly doesn't burn, it smolders. Roiling black toxic killer fumes. Dioxins and heavy metal residues, you know, arsenic and copper and lead, plenty of chemicals with multi-syllabic names like phenyl poly-carbonate cyo-fryo your brainiac chloride, nothing you wouldn't put in Gerber's baby food jars, of course, nothing you couldn't roast hot dogs on...

The country, to the newcomers, is overwhelmingly *vast*. In the suburbs you'd be *sued*. In the suburb they all frown on killing the neighbors with black toxic mushroom clouds of seriously poisonous gases, I don't care if your attorney claims it was only dirty diapers.

But in the country, in the Outback, in the Hinterlands, in the Big Empty, well, the rules expand to meet the distant horizon… Tired of that car? Burn it. Trailer on its last legs? Torch it. Need to get rid of… Well, practically *anything?* Douse it with gasoline, set it on fire, drag out the old TV's, the sofas, the plastic pop bottles, but *wait* until the wind is blowing *my* way, why don'tcha? Someday we'll tell the grandkids, oh, those were the days. The sun turning romantic blood red through the afternoon smoke, the sweet aroma of styrenes and butyl carbonates. The muffled pop of chemical explosions. I know, it's politically incorrect now, but it's something you younguns won't get to experience: when the country was country and *not* a damned Transfer Station.

Enough's Enough

A little further up the metaphorical road, and way up the proverbial ladder to success, folks are doing pretty good for themselves. Their houses are running hundreds of thousands of dollars and their cars cost more'n my whole property cost me awhile back when the economy wasn't the engine it is today. All I can figure is they must have big salary jobs to pay for it all.

I've been a South Ender so long I guess I've lost touch with wages and salaries and stock options and second mortgages and investment strategies. Cause I can't imagine what it must take to own a half million dollar home and send the kids to law schools back east and drive a BMW SUV when gas is at an all-time high at the Elger Bay pumps. And still have something left over for plasma TV's and multiple computer stations and satellite links and every electronic gizmo and software that's ever been made or soon will be.

A long time back we came to the South End to escape all that. Fired the accounting team and grew a garden. But here it comes right back, a way of life with enough credit to buy my piddly little garden a thousand times over, pave it with blacktop and build a gated vacation home where the squashes used to free range. I think the new neighbors are praying I'll move along. Sell the farm and move somewhere peaceful in the Ozarks. And it isn't like I haven't thought about it...

But awhile back I decided this was home. Just the shack, a great mizzus, a woods I can hike in, a beach I can get to. And time enough to do it. Down at the slippery slopes of the South End, we may not have much, but we got enough. And one thing we learned here is that enough is plenty... That's a piece of knowledge some folks never learn and a peace of mind you *can't* take to the bank.

VISIT

THE FABLED

SOUTH END

WHERE TIME STANDS STILL
AND THE STILLS STILL STAND

SOUTH END TOURISM BUREAU

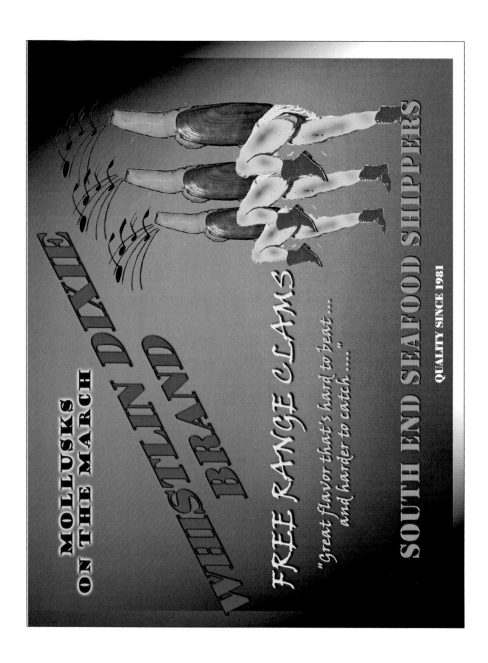

MOLLUSKS
ON THE MARCH

WHISTLIND DIXIE
BRAND

FREE RANGE CLAMS

"Great flavor that's hard to beat ...
and harder to catch ...."

SOUTH END SEAFOOD SHIPPERS

QUALITY SINCE 1981

137

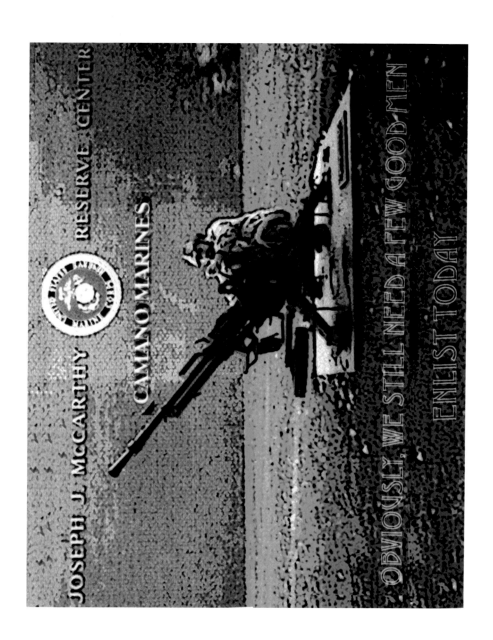

END OF THE ROAD GALLERY

YOUR FULL SERVICE ART DEALER

STATION MANAGER SKEETER DADDLE

ATLAS TIRES

LUBRICATION

STANDARD STATIONS, INC.

DADA DIAGNOSTICS
CUBIST CLUTCH WORK
WATERCOLOR COOLANT FLUSH
9 POINTILLIST TRANSMISSION CHECK

BAROQUE BRAKES
OIL AND ACRYLIC CHANGE
SURREALIST STRUTS
POST-MODERN MUFFLERS

BAUHAUS BATTERIES
ABSTRACT ALIGNMENTS
STAINED GLASS GAS SHOCKS
IMPRESSIONIST EMISSION INSPECTION

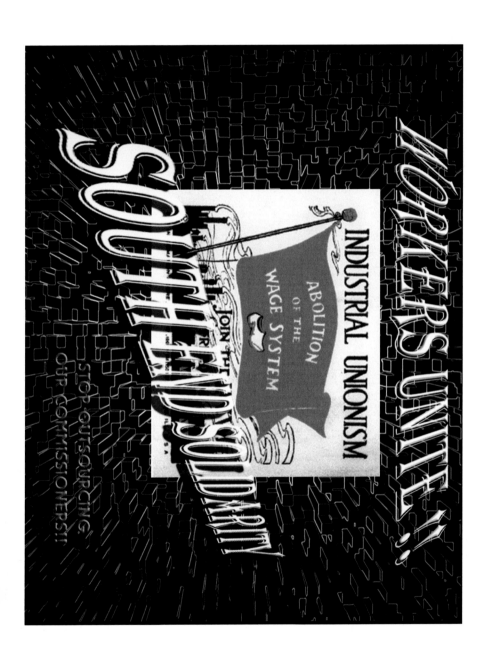

Apocalypse Then: After the Rapture

Them that died be the lucky ones.

Long John Silver

No Joking

I was taking a flight out of South End International last week. Wasn't *too* long ago when it was just a grass runway in the middle of the old growth nettles where drug smugglers and rich retirees could slide in beneath the radar for quick midnight landings.

Those seat of the pants days are long gone now, replaced with heavy security and baggage checks and long lines that make the checkout gridlock at Elger Bay Grocery look like an express lane. South End International, of course, might *seem* like a backwash hub, something a hi-jacking air terrorist might see as easy pickings, but he better think twice is all I can say.

Last time through the metal detectors, the security boys had my grammaw stripped near down to her petticoats and I have no doubt if she'd been Moslem instead of Baptist and she'd been 60 years younger and she'd been male and looked a little more ticked off, well sir, they'd have had my grammaw flying in the baggage compartment.

These are nervous times we live in. And even on the South End we got to be vigilant now. Used to be you couldn't make Hi-Jacking jokes without the air marshals dragging you off—now *all* joking is outlawed. Just as well... You stand in line with a hundred people holding their shoes and their belts in one hand, their carry-on luggage in the other, their photo ID and their boarding pass in their teeth, their pants falling down and their grammaw being strip-searched for bombs in her brassiere, you'd have a hard time finding anything funny in that.

Frankenfood

Ma brought home a bag of some kind of snack food the other day—and being the literary sort, I got to reading the warning label and ingredient list on the packaging. This one said it had no transfats, no artificial preservatives, no cholesterol, no genetically engineered sweeteners, no antibiotics, no irradiated parts and was *not* known by the State of California to cause cancer.

I was reassured, of course, but oddly enough my appetite had vanished completely.

On the South End we still grow our food. We still catch some of it. And we raise the rest. Oh, we use a lot of manure and lord knows where those crabs have been partying and acid rain's probably in the raspberries and the clams are laying where the neighbor's drainfield heads.

It worries me, though, what the so-called food industry is dreaming up. Fake fats and phony sugar. They make us obese then they figure out the diet remedy. Pretty soon we'll get potato chips with beta blockers, candy bars with acne medications, coca-cola with Ritalin. The food industry and the pharmaceuticals and the geneticists, it's a match made in heaven.

I told Ma don't buy any more of that pure stuff, all unadulterated and lacking flavor. I want organic I'll go back in the woods and gnaw on nettles. Course when the food boys figure out an anti-itch additive, we'll all be eating the tickly little taste treats. No transfats. No greasy aftertaste. Just 100% natural goodness processed and packaged for your culinary pleasure. Mmm mmm good... Can't wait for the poison ivy chip dip...

Logging Missionaries

The South End's got our fair share of Bible Thumpers, Pulpit Pounders, Praise the Lorders, all of em setting out readerboard highway sign testimonials and bumpersticker halleluiahs. They're good folks really, but they think me and my cronies are the Spawn of Satan.

Course, so do I, but I stick it out anyway, figuring, I'm too old to convert these fellas to my brand of holiness. I reckon I'll just serve as a Role Model for these sinners—a Light and a Way— and when the right time comes, they'll reach out like Drowning Men for a lifesaver.

You should know I haven't saved a one of em yet... Religion's like a lot of things. Sometimes timing's everything. My old pard, Guitar Bob and me were down in the hollers cutting up a pile of old logs for firewood a friend had stacked up ten feet high and let get slimy as a greased pig. We were up top with our chainsaws making a racket like two speedboats in love, stepping as gingerly as two he-men can without actually dancing together, when all of a sudden the whole pile let loose and those logs and Bob and me and the saws, we all commenced to coming down together. Now I was sure we were going to be crushed in between this avalanche of wood like possums under a tractor trailer.

I don't mind telling you, I was scared. I was real scared. But hell, we're South Enders and we waltzed down those snot slick logs like we were walking down an escalator in a mall, and when we hit bottom, we looked at each other to see if the other fella was alive… and well, he was and our saws were still raring to go—although, honestly, I felt a little wobbly and a drink right then would have been greatly appreciated.

And that's when we noticed the car full of suits that had pulled in the drive all big-eyed staring out the window. You see a car full of suits, it's got to be one of three things: either the realtors have got the wrong house, or the FBI have got the wrong suspect, or the missionaries have got the wrong two sinners to convert.

Like I say, timing's the real key. The Head Reverend popped out and said that was practically a miracle what they just saw—which is how I felt *exactly*—a miracle, and would we be interested in discussing Scripture? I said, well sir, we just got Saved a few minutes ago and it wouldn't be fair to all the other Lost Souls down here on the South End if we were to get Saved twice so maybe we best pass.

The moral is you got to hit a fella when he's *down* on his luck if you want to convert em to your way of thinking. You live in a little slice of Heaven like the South End, you're Rolling a rock up a long hill if you're trying to bring these sinners around toward personal salvation. Me, I'm willing to wait on all the rest of these wayward souls. No place else to go, I guess. And all the time in the world…

The Next Frontier

I sometimes think all of us here represent the last wave of American Westward Expansion. We paddled across to these islands, looked out our cabin windows one morning and realized this may be as far as we can go. We got to the tail end of these islands at the far end of this continent at the last hour of the millennium.

I don't know about you all, but I was looking for one last chance to live an earlier American Dream, the one where cheap land was still available and opportunity was something you could grab with two strong hands. I was looking for the same thing the pioneers were: a fresh start. A little breathing room. New ground. I think that's what America *is:* The opportunity—the Potential—to recreate yourself. To hitch up the conestoga and leave the past behind. To make your mistakes and move on. To *always* feel like you can start over...

Some folks might think, well, you people sure picked a box canyon to homestead. The only place left to go is a long cold swim. End of the road. End of America. Last stand... But the thing about living at the tail end of an island at the end of the 20th Century at the edge of the continental shelf is that it has a

Romance, you see. It has an epic appeal. An imaginative Spark. It's a place a Dream can set roots. You're surrounded by volcanoes and mountain ranges, the tides bring something new every day, the winds ride the sails of giant cedars and fir trees older than America itself. You can't help but feel your spirit soar. You can't *not* dream large. You can't live a day here and not feel a living, breathing *connection* to the awesome majesty of this place.

Ironically, from here, from the island's tail, we learned nothing is really impossible. We learned the water is no moat, the mountains are no barrier. We learned the ends are really means. We learned this place is a beginning and we know if we have to, we'll grow something akin to wings and we'll learn a new kind of flying.

Mouse Abuse:
the Unspoken Tragedy

Call me a curmudgeon, but I hate computers. Oh, I know, they're gonna transform the world and even the South End. I'm not some Luddite who wants to take an ax handle to the Spinning Jenny and stop the Industrial Revolution in its tracks so we can all stay serfs and peasants and grow cabbage for the King's table forever.

The computer's gonna put men on Mars and I'm all for it. I even got a list made up for who I want sent first. And computers are gonna map all the genomes so we can make purple ketchup the natural way without food dye. And I suspect computers will play banjo and fiddle before long and the South End String Band will once again be back to normal—meaning, out of work.

No, what bothers me about a computer is how it already makes me do its bidding. Mix up a number or a letter or about any damn thing and it won't do anything. It's like I planted a garden and if I didn't space the seeds just so and say the magic words, none of em would sprout. It's like a bipolar mule. Great when it wants to be, something you want to beat when it ain't.

I confess to terrible things when I got that mouse by its electronic tail and it doesn't do what I want. Bam bam bam on the desk. Bam bam bam against the wall. Doesn't matter one bit to the computer—although I feel a whole lot better.

Kids are gonna grow up thinking this is the way the world works. Cross every 'T', dot every 'I'. Read the directions. Follow the rules. I think computers are programming *us*. They already got me doing things the mizzus couldn't get me to do in 25 years of marriage. Maybe it isn't the mouse that's getting shook by the tail after all…

The Road Taken

Some folks look back at their lives, you know, in these advancing years, and wish they'd done things a little different. Maybe gotten a job, earned some money, a little respect, a nest egg for the hard years waiting up around the corner.

Me, I'm an ornery old South Ender, and one thing I've learned, maybe the only thing I've learned, is *not* to look back. Don't do it! I mean, nostalgia's a fine thing, but not for trying to figure out what fork in all those crooked roads we were lost on might've made a difference.

Course they made a difference. But hellfire, they could've made everything *worse*. Only a damn fool sits around regretting everything they've done. Better to think tomorrow's another fork. Now that I'm so all fired smart from all those missed opportunities and mistakes and near misses, that fork in the road tomorrow's going to look like an interstate to success and happiness.

Truth is, down at the South End, which is at the tail end of a skinny chicken neck island, the forks were few and what we learned was they all ended up here, some just took a little longer. What you learned was the route sometimes isn't the end-all be-all, it's the song on the radio, or the season you're traveling, or the hitchhiker you picked up or just the thoughts in your head.

They're not going to come up with a GPS for life. Too bad for the folks who want to plan their trip, figure every gas station, motel and restaurant from here to the grave. Better, I think, to enjoy the surprises. A bad meal usually won't kill you. Or a lumpy motel mattress once in awhile. Success isn't navigating a map without getting hopelessly lost. Real success is enjoying the drive. We're all lost, you want to know the truth. Us South Enders are lucky—we don't Mind being lost.

Smog Alert

The mizzus and me burn wood for our heat. For survival, I guess it's fair to say… Most of the South End does too… Used to be we *all* did down here. We had that WHOOPS debacle back in the early 80's, nuclear power plants all set to go, then they realized all five plants probably weren't really needed, so we mothballed em, the investors took a whipping and our electric bills that were so cheap when we generated power off the steady rainfall of our gutters, the bills went sky high.

So for awhile *everybody* ran out and bought an airtight wood stove and before long we were saving money *big time…*

Unless you deducted the chainsaw and the cost of the stove and the zero clearance stainless steel pipe through the roof and the splitting maul and the pickup truck and the carrying cart and the gas and oil and the trips to the chiropractor and the back surgery…

Country Living. Looked like Pittsburg about the turn of the Last Century, belching smoke and ash. Chimney fires and trailers burnt up. Those were the days… Nowadays we've cut most of the South End forests down, the EPA has tight stove standards and the County frowns on wood stoves period. Pellet stoves ditto. Burn bans come around more and more frequent and it's only a matter of time before burning wood will be a heinous criminal offense punishable by fines and jail time, and, in me and the mizzus' case, serious frostbite.

Mercifully, the radiant heat of our love will keep us warm. Good luck to everybody else.

1984:
Caution—Objects May Appear Closer

A lot of folks pine for the good old days *before* technology made privacy a thing of the past. George Orwell never dreamed half the stuff we got now. Not only the government can track you cradle to grave, corporations can do it too. They know your buying preferences, they know your income, they know your personal history, they can track you by credit card, by Social Security number, by cellphone, by e-mail and by GPS.

Some folks don't mind. If somebody keeps track of their grocery purchases, happy reading. If companies want to sell their name and buying habits to other companies, well, that's free trade. If the government needs to see if they're talking to Osama Bin Laden, go ahead, listen in. If their employer wants to monitor their e-mails, hey, they're the boss. If surveillance cameras are set up on every corner, why not, they're not doing anything illegal. If they check a book out of the library, okay by them if the government checks it out too. If satellite photography gets much better, well, they can shut the blinds.

We folks on the South End are accustomed to privacy intrusions. We had a party line most of our lives and the grapevine all of it. Gossip makes government look like a piker so far. My neighbors knew my buying habits, my whereabouts, *most* of my criminal activity and *all* my comings and goings.

I suppose it gripes me that QFC and Safeway and Haggens and most of the chains keep track of my vegetable addictions. But Tyee Store always knows my favorite adult beverages and *what's more important*, they know my face. If I ever thought the hat was a disguise, I was mistaken...

Terrorists Seize Newsroom

We're getting to be a country of scaredy-cats. They found a cougar on the island a few years back and you best believe folks were nervous. Eat their chihuahuas, eat their kitty cat, eat the mizzus.

September 11th those two planes hit the Trade Towers and scared the pants off us. I still know folks who won't fly in an airplane. For awhile people wouldn't go to a mall. Or a movie theater. Tyee Store.

We're afraid of terrorists in Sears. SARS in airplanes. Airplanes in office buildings. Office buildings higher'n three stories. We're afraid of our own shadows and John Ashcroft shadowing us. We're afraid of epidemics, foreigners, unemployment. We drive SUV's, we carry mace, we don't trust strangers. Hell, we don't trust anybody. We're afraid of being robbed, being mugged, being raped and being killed. We see it every night on the TV news. We see it five times every night on TV news. We see it in the movies, on television shows, in magazines, in books. Future archeologists and historians are gonna wonder how we didn't kill ourselves off in a month.

The odds of being stabbed or shot or killed by a serial killer seem small to me, but I guess it's why we buy lottery tickets... Poor math skills. Down at the South End we don't lock our doors. The only deadbolt I got was off my '50 pickup overtorquing the engine head back on. Now there's something to be afraid of...

Bad things happen, I know that. But if you're always worrying they will, you'll hide under a blanket and miss all the good that could've happened. Most folks are decent, honest, kind, upstanding people. I know that because they're my neighbors and I know my neighbors. We're mostly afraid of the things we don't know so my advice is: get to know the neighbors. Course, if the TV crews are always showing up in your neighborhood, I got some additional advice...

Born on the South End

I ran into a rough character in the hardware store the other day. He had on a black T-shirt with a rebel flag and it said on the back *U.S. Born Native*. I guess the Confederate flag threw me. Sort of like tattooing: *Native South Ender*, then writing next to it: *Long Live Utsalady*.

I know this guy. If he lived in France, he'd hate the Moslems immigrating in, taking his car wash job. If he was in California, he'd hate the Mexicans taking his cucumber picking job. If he lived here, he'd hate us transplants for stealing his high paying nettle baling job. My neighbor, who *is* a native South Ender, hates the newcomers ruining the Homeland. When I remind him that he makes his living building em houses, he just shakes his head and says if he didn't build em, somebody else would and it would still get ruined.

I'm one of those poor huddled masses that immigrated in. I did all the crummy low paying jobs the locals wouldn't stoop to. You know, ditch digging, husk shovelling on the Twin City Food graveyard, school bus driving, stained glass work. Degrading stuff. Humiliating. But I survived. And I learned the customs of the South End. I was part of the melting pot, sort of the residue on the bottom of the pan. But I became a South Ender and I suspect the South End is different because I came. Maybe not better... But different.

America is like the South End in most ways. Folks like to think Tom Jefferson and Ben Franklin and the radical boys meant for it to stay the way they first interpreted it. But they forget that the Founding Fathers were some real-deal revolutionaries. Those guys who invented America sure as hell didn't swagger into the mercantile wearing a sign on their topcoat next to the Union Jack reading: *Born Citizen*. When the South End shuts the gate on newcomers, I say it might just be time to be a newcomer again...

Partisan Weather

I know a lot of you are worried about Global Warming. And I know some of you don't believe it's true. I know some folks are worried about the next Ice Age. And others think we're still in it.

We got El Nina years and La Nina years. We got ozone depletion, greenhouse gas accretion, we got soft tundra and oozing glaciers, we got more hurricanes and record setting cold weather. We got record setting hot weather and jet streams hopping north and south so fast it's like a bipolar meteorological condition.

It's getting hard to know how to dress. Layers, I guess. Gortex layers. It's that or Biospheric Domes. Put the cities under Pyrex. Big thermostat the City Council can fight over. Yell at each other for forgetting to turn it down at night.

Personally I think all this weather talk is good. You can't talk politics anymore everybody's so polarized. I just worry when we blame the other party for the weather. What're we gonna talk about then? Republican caused monsoons? Hurricane Hilary? The Bush Blizzard of 2007? The Democratic Killer Heat Wave?

I don't know about all of you, but I think that will have some serious global consequences. Shrinking dialogues, frozen conversations, stormy relationships and violent domestic ventings. Fox Weather might predict calm sunny days every day of the week, but for the rest of us, it means no more conversational crutches. No more, 'Hot enuff for ya?' instead of 'How about that War in Iraq?' No more 'I'm ready for it to quit raining any decade now' instead of 'You got an opinion on that government surveillance spying?'

So if you're complacent about the global warming debate, imagine a Weather Channel that looks like Chechnya. Maybe you'll rethink it.

The Message
is the Medium

Our attention spans are shrinking faster'n Ma's favorite wool sweater when I washed it. They got a cell phone now that'll sell you one minute installments of teeny weeny shows. Used to be, sitting in the dentist's office, you'd leaf through a magazine a couple months old, usually something with lots of pictures. Now you pull out your cell phone and enjoy the wait buying made-for-phone movies and video games.

Cinemascope it ain't. Us old fogies buy TV's the size of drive-in theater screens. Our kids are putting movie screens in their SUV's. And their kids are gonna be watching Gone With The Wind on an LED monitor the size of a guitar pick. In 500 one minute installments. And I assume the next generation will have implants in their eyelids so they can watch *something* 24/7. They'll bill you thru the chip in your brain.

Now I'm all for increased efficiency. And *my* attention span isn't what it *was*. But there's something strange about a TV at my gas pump, spitting out a little sports, a little news and the great deal on the microwave fatball on sale inside. The other day I used the restroom in the Bon Macy in downtown Seattle and Gomorrah. That's right, a tiny TV screen right over the urinal. A woman the size of a hummingbird was talking to me...

Now, am I out of touch? Am I just being old-fashioned? Am I squeamish about pee-ing directly at a woman who's suffering the indignity of this supposedly private moment?

I honestly don't know. But I know this: I don't *need* a TV on my phone, a TV on my watch, a TV in the shop, a TV in the truck, a TV in my head... And I certainly, unequivocally, absolutely, *do not* need a TV over a urinal...

Even if it does take me a little longer these days...

Self Medication: The Doctor Is In

Everyday you can read in the paper how health care costs are going through the roof, no way to slow em down short of hanging the trial lawyers and making the doctors swear an oath of poverty. A lot of folks moving down to the South End were real surprised we don't have clinics or pharmacies or emergency rooms. They're paying all this money for insurance premiums and all they get for it is the flickering hope they'll survive the 40 mile ambulance ride with the Mabana Fire Station volunteers.

Used to be we were thankful for even that. Me, I still am. When *my* checkout time comes, I don't want six months in the Pain Motel with machines keeping me ticking and Ma going broke. I guess, though, we *all* want to go to heaven, but nobody wants to die to get there. And nowadays they got the wonders of the pharmaceutical companies advertised on TV, in magazines, everywhere. Cure nearly everything that ails ya. Getting old never looked so easy. Ask your doctor. Oh, and better buy stock in Glaxo and Phizer.

The wonders of modern science don't come cheap. A lot of us on the South End don't have health insurance so we have to suck it up. I'd like to think our homemade therapies are tried and true.

Me, I suspect most of us are a lot better off *without* advertisers prescribing our remedies and HMO's running expensive tests and all of us worrying most of the time if we're gonna live to see the sun come up or we're gonna have quality love-making at 90.

There's a time honored saying we got down at the South End: Old age ain't for sissies. Although I expect any day now they'll find a cure for both… Cost an arm and a leg… Ask your surgeon.

Fast Food, Fast Fuel

We been watching a new trend developing lately down here on the South End: Biodiesel. Taking farmlands and using it to grow fuel instead of food. Now, I don't know what *your* rig gets per gallon, but I guess most of us Americans who want a Bradley Fighting Vehicle to go shopping in war-torn Stanwoodopolis, don't care *what* it costs in gas so long as it's cheaper per gallon than designer bottled water.

I hear a lot of complaining now that gas prices are at an all time high. I guess we thought a democratic Iraq would so grateful they'd give us free oil and we'd *all* be driving full size Hummers. I even heard an oil company last week complaining they didn't have the money for any more cleanup penalties from the Valdez spill. Tough times for all of us, I guess.

So maybe it *is* the right time to take food and turn it into fuel. Gas stations will look more like a fast food drive-up. Tomato diesel, hi octane fryer fat, corn on the cob unleaded, you want to supersize that fill-up, ma'am?

The burger chains are already teamed up with the gas stations on this. Way ahead of us. Pump the deep fat fryers into you *and* your car. A full service station means they got a health clinic in back to handle clogged arteries, get you back on the road in no time.

Cutting down on the driving or cutting down on the car size or cutting down on the calories just isn't the South End way, I guess. If it means cutting down our old growth nettle forests to make biodiesel, by god, we're gonna do it. Might as well—we'll need the acreage for the new autobahn into Stanwoodopolis.

South End
Doppelgänger

Down at the laboratories of the South End industrial parks, our scientists are working 24/7 to catch up with the head start all those government subsidized research labs got on us. You might think we're at a disadvantage, but you haven't factored in the leg up our innovative crew of experimenters get from the creative ricochet of living in proximity to all the South End artists. Practically a Petri dish of teeming mutating e-volved thinking. Ordinary folks should probably suit up in bio-hazard gear. That, or vaccinate themselves with high dosage Prozac.

Our teams of specialists are working on stem cell research. You take some cell tissues, see, and you train em like circus fleas to behave like brains or bones or eyeballs or whatever you need right then and you give the patient a spoonful or two and I tell you what: you got a whole new lease on life, and if you got insurance, well sir, you might as well grow a few spare parts while you're at it.

Now, we got folks who picket the lab. Neighbors who think we're in the Frankenstein business, cloning mice and sheep and two headed humans. I tell em we're not cloning, we're stem celling. Stem cell selling, actually. Nothing to worry about. We're curing diseases. We're making a little money.

Cloning—now that's putting a hard edge on it, don't ya think? Stem cells, that isn't a real person, exactly. Dumb as a rock, most stem cells, but the protestors say so are most South Enders—which, I have to admit, is a pretty convincing argument. Until you think of the lives that could be saved. And the money too, coincidentally. What *if*, I say, we could make stem cells *smarter* than us South Enders. What's so wrong with *that*? And *they* say, your little friend would have *you* doing the chores while they did the thinking.

I got to admit, it's a complicated issue. Personally I think we better go slow. Make my little friend not too smart. Maybe just smart enough to do my chores...

South End
Literacy Foundation

Now a lot of folks think the South End is mostly a bunch of illiterate yahoos who wouldn't know a library from the Uff Da Shoppe, who couldn't tell a Hemingway from a hemi and who think Beethoven's Fifth is a jug of moonshine. The truth is, those balmy evenings we gather on the front porch to speculate on the meaning of the cosmos, to discourse on politics and the Machiavellian intricacies in that nasty run for county commissioner, or to gripe about the Keynesian economic ramifications of the Fed's latest interest rate manipulation, we often cast back to articles and books and Internet research to make our blurry points.

We never had a library on the South End, other than the 25¢ used romance novels all dog-eared in the back of Bartlett's Tyee Grocery. So we've come to depend on Stanwoodopolis' fine Biblioteca to nourish our literary and cultural needs. The Stanwood Library, for those of you who just fell off the turnip truck coming in from Smokey Point, used to be a building that was the Stillaguamish Band Hall the early part of last century. It was given to the city and jacked up and moved it into town. The first bookmobile. Around 1970 it moved again where now it's a gun club up by Cedarhome, the only rootin tootin shootin gallery library in America. That's right, shooting range, target practice, high velocity, semi-automatic, skeets, snub-nosed .38's, double barrel shotguns—a Gun Club. Substitute your library card for an NRA card. Check out books and ammo at the same time.

I bet it's the only library in America with a target range out back. The penalty for overdue books, I suspect, must be pretty severe. Give the offender a cigarette and a blindfold. Make sure it doesn't happen twice… Most libraries try to keep the noise to a minimum. Not Stanwood. Neither one really, although the replacement one in town won't allow gunfire. Not that you could hear above the kids shouting if someone did shoot off their shotgun.

I like the idea of a gun club library. It's real American. You won't find gun club libraries practically anywhere else. Baghdad maybe these days… Andrew Carnegie, the steel magnate who made a bazillion bucks paying his workers next to nothing, but who was generous enough later on to buy libraries for a lot of cities; he used to have Pinkerton men shoot his striking workers, so a gun library has some kind of precedent going for it. Keeps the librarians from asking for pay increases, if nothing else. Save Stanwoodopolis a little money…

Like I said, the library we got now replaced the gun club library back in the early 70's. The local literati raised their own money and they built it the way we build most stuff around these parts. With volunteers, the same way we're doing it this time around. In the 80's they built the addition. More volunteerism. More pride in the community. The old library has grown a mite cramped since 10,000 newcomers have joined the neighborhood. I haven't sat in front of a computer yet, not with all the school kids playing video games and watching porn. Which is why I'm nostalgic for the old card catalogue.

Used to be when we outgrew a library we built another, but times change and Stanwoodopolis doesn't mind saving money by staying crammed. I guess they figure all the condos and apartments and developments they keep putting in at the new annexations are filled with new folks who are mostly illiterate.

Down at the South End we don't know much, but we know this: A community is nothing more and nothing less than its hopes and dreams and aspirations. A library might just be the heart and soul of a place. A good one has a lot more than truck repair manuals. It has art and music and architecture and history. A library isn't a roomful of books. It's every song we ever sang, every poem we ever spoke, every picture we ever painted, every history ever written, every story ever told. It's our cultural DNA. It's who we are and it's all right there.

I hear folks ask all the time why do we need a new library? Why spend one more red cent? Why not put it in an old store and call it good enough? Being an ornery, cantankerous old South Ender, I got an opinion on that and it's this: A library is a *symbol*. Sort of like the South End itself, it's a metaphor. It's a portal to the knowledge of the world and the gateway to our own future. In a way, it's a shrine to learning. A learning that doesn't stop at high school or college or *any* school for that matter. It's where we go to be inspired. It's where our kids can see what we thought was important. Knowledge. Culture. History. Community. Our community. They walk into that new library, they understand what our dreams for them are, what hopes we have for them, what possibilities we want them to have, what a promising future is open to them. And to us.

Course, we could keep sending em down to the old library. Watch out for the giant people-eating clam lurking out front by the book drop, though. Or send em up to the gun club library. Better not make too much noise, if you know what's good for you squirts... Personally, I think they deserve better. And so do we. On the South End we got a saying, a man who don't shoe his horses better have two pair for himself. He's gonna be walking real soon.

Immanence Until Proven Guilty

Most folks pity us, I suspect. Every winter the windstorms knock our power out for days. They can't imagine much worse. They ask what in blue tarnation do you do? No TV. No DVD movies. No news from the outside world. Just the godawful sound of the wind and the waves. The woodstove crackling and us kids forced to entertain ourselves. Don't it drive us to madness? Don't it make us want to move to town? Don't we start killing the neighbors?

I used to think, sitting early mornings by my big woodstove waiting for the coffee water to boil, my dog, old Dr. Gonzo, watching me sleepy-eyed on the hearth with the cat curled snug up against her, all of us waiting for daylight and that teapot singing a note like a banjo's high G, I used to think: we all know what's been lost, the sound of kids rustling up, hopping on barefeet across a cold plank floor, getting up, getting going, the smell of woodsmoke curling out of a chimney, the slow feel of sun coming up through the fog in the firs and the whole world slowly reappearing, wet and dripping like a newborn thing just spanked to life, that first intake of breath, everything waiting. We think we don't have time for this anymore, but we know we had it once. We know it's right there for us to see again, coming awake out of the dawn.

The mizzus says I ought to give it up, but I say I'll be damned if I'll watch the South End get took over by the suburbs, folks who could just as easy be in Atlanta or Denver, who never care that the little house across from the Fire Hall was the old school, or there used to be a Bucklin's Store right down the road, or the families that started farming way back are still here, that Bernie Road is named after Bernie Dallman and Dallman Road is too and Bernie's family's still here in the neighborhood.

People are always asking me if I'm one of them South End Old Timers. Now I know I look about two wobbly steps from pitching into the Pioneer Cemetery, but the truth is, I'm no Old Timer. To be an Old Timer, you got to live here a hundred years or more and be able to remember when the road to the South End was a muddy two lane rut. We got a couple of em on the South End, people born and raised here. America's a country of immigrants and so's the South End. We're passing through, most of us. What matters is respecting the past. Knowing what came before. Walking gentle among the ghosts. Roots don't mean much. History either. Maybe it should... But you ought to respect what came before us, whether it's natives or pioneers. We're all immigrants in this world and that's the truth of it. We're all just traveling through. But pay some attention. There's bones under us. There's history under us and around us. And I say you ought to turn off the damn TV long enough to pay proper mind to it.

I think deep down we know what's missing. We know this too:

We won't ever find it surfing channels. We won't buy it in a mall. We won't drive by it on the freeway going to work. It ain't coming door to door. And we sure as hell won't win it in the Lottery…

But then again, I'm just an ornery old banjo picker living out his days on the South End and maybe the mizzus is right, I should just let it go… If you're ever down this chicken neck end of the woods, stop by the porch and visit the mizzus and me. We aren't going anywhere. You all know how to find it.

Apocalypse Then: After the Rapture

"Jug's empty, boys, time to face the music..."

Skeeter Daddle, on way too many nights.